Cancer
and
Positivity

A musician's journey through
illness, learning and teaching

Paul Harris

Cancer and Positivity
First published in 2019 by Queen's Temple Publications

ISBN 9780955247385

QT200

Queen's Temple Publications, 15 Mallard Drive, Buckingham, MK18 1GJ

Contents

Acknowledgements

Having journeyed through this experience and the attendant myriad of emotions, the words 'thank you' can never really express the depth of gratitude one feels to those who have been part of it. The very special thanks to all those below are deeply felt.

The wonderful doctors and nurses at my local surgery and of the various hospitals I've spent time at, but most of all those of the EPCTU at the exceptional Churchill Hospital in Oxford.

All my very special friends, many of whom are included in the pages that follow, who have supported me through the journey.

Richard Crozier, who initially suggested I keep a journal. What a very good idea that turned out to be! Unloading my thoughts, worries, feelings, on to paper was wonderful therapy. It put them somewhere else.

Some particular friends who have read, commented on and helped prepare the contents of this book. They know who they are!

Sue Clarke who has done a completely brilliant job in turning my scribblings into this very special book.

Lymphoma Action and
The Churchill Hospital Charity
for their support and to whom
all proceeds of this book will go.

Faber Music, my publishers,
for their wonderful support.

Biography

After studies at the Royal Academy of Music and the University of London, Paul Harris has now established an international reputation as one of the UK's leading music educationalists. He studied the clarinet with Professor John Davies, winning the August Manns Prize for outstanding performance. He then went on to study music education at the University of London where he was a pupil of Professor Keith Swanwick. He now has over six hundred publications to his name dealing with a vast array of subjects mostly concerning music education. His *Music Teacher's Companion* (co-written with Richard Crozier), won the UK's MIA Best New Book award and his series *Improve Your Theory!* the Music Teacher Best Print Resource Award. In addition he has written many works ranging from countless short education pieces to seven concertos, a ballet and a children's opera. He has also co-authored (with Anthony Meredith) biographies of the composers Sir Malcolm Arnold, Malcolm Williamson and Sir Richard Rodney Bennett. He writes regularly for many of the major international music magazines and is in great demand as a workshop leader and adjudicator in the UK and across the globe. He performs regularly and is also an examiner. In 2006 Paul Harris established the annual Malcolm Arnold Festival in the composer's hometown of Northampton. He has created and continues to develop **Simultaneous Learning**, his highly acclaimed approach to instrumental and singing teaching that has found support all over the world.

Author's note

I wrote this journal over a 10-month period recounting my extraordinary journey through non-Hodgkin lymphoma. As a writer and teacher, I spent much of that time thinking, so the following text features a number of thoughts of a more philosophical nature, particularly about music teaching and learning, which has always been my life's passion. I hope these thoughts, which appear with a thought bubble and in italics, will be of interest to all readers.

August 2018
Friday 31
A retrospective thought

I'm on an aeroplane flying back from two days working with music teachers in Dubai. This trip represents a major landmark in my life. I've just spent the best part of a year with cancer and this is my return to life as it used to be. It's my return, to some extent, to the person I was. But not entirely. The experience I've had has been truly life-changing. What follows is a story of illness on the one hand, and on the other, learning and teaching: countervailing energies which, for me, have all become intimately and profoundly related.

My hotel in Dubai

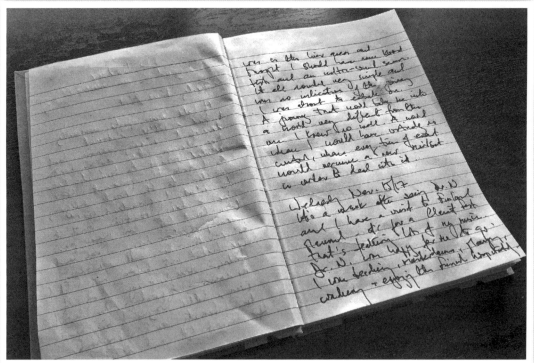

I actually began the journal as a written document, though as time passed, some of it was dictated into my phone and some was typed straight into my laptop. What follows is a combination of all three methods.

November 2017

Tuesday 9 *It begins*

It all began quite innocently. I had a little abdominal discomfort – nothing particularly concerning, but I've always taken any health problem (happily, very few to date) straight to an expert. So I took the ten-minute walk up to my local surgery for what I considered would be a fairly routine visit. Given that, in these post-family-doctor days, it's rare ever to see the same doctor twice, I was sent to Dr Andrew Noden. We hadn't met before but I liked Andrew immediately, with his friendly, no-nonsense approach. The discomfort, I told him, was a little vague, both in intensity and its location. He investigated, decided it was in the liver area, and recommended some blood tests and an ultrasound scan.

It all sounded fairly unthreatening; there was no indication of the journey I was about to embark upon. A journey that would take me into a world so different from the one I knew so well. A world where I would have virtually no control, where nearly every turn of event would require a whole new mindset in order to deal with it. A world where one's identity dissolves into an entirely new one. Where one assumes the role of patient and literally and unconditionally puts one's life into the hands of a group of strangers. But it's extraordinary how we can adjust. Extraordinary how we *can* find new mindsets. When real necessity dictates, we can be very flexible, open-minded and accommodating.

I made the decision very early on that I would share as much as I could with friends and colleagues. This journal is a consequence of that decision. I also decided, on the other hand, not to share it on social media. But it seems to me that keeping serious illness to yourself is not helpful. Some may think they have more control of the situation if they suppress or conceal it. For others it may be shame, fear or even embarrassment that prohibits sharing.

For those who do worry about sharing such experiences – whether illness or anything else – I think it's worth re-considering. The pros, in most cases, significantly outweigh the cons. Of course, when it comes to serious illness, it is wise to tell people sensitively and gauge their reaction thoughtfully and caringly, which then determines how to proceed. (Just as in any effective teaching interaction, in fact.) But engaging with people gives them the opportunity to help and support you – a problem shared is a problem halved. I'd go a bit further … a problem shared (especially a problem like serious illness), enables very significant support and comfort through the journey, which in turn can have a very significant impact upon the outcome.

Anyway, that first innocuous visit to the GP was the start of a journey to places I couldn't possibly have foreseen. This is the story of that journey.

. . .

An intermission

A week after seeing my GP I had a long-standing visit to Finland in the diary: to attend an exciting Clarinet Festival where a lot of my music was to be studied and played. Dr Noden was happy for me to go. I was due to perform, teach, give masterclasses and coach ensembles.

I learnt much about the amazing Finnish education system during this visit and became immediately impatient to talk about it wherever I could. It is a system that is not based on limiting and frustrating one-size-fits-all principles. A system that isn't based on interminable exams; that doesn't require homework to be set; where there are no hierarchical structures in schools – just a head and a deputy head and teachers who seem to thoroughly enjoy teaching. All this resulting in students who seem to thoroughly enjoy learning. And, most importantly, there are very few children with mental health issues as a consequence of their schooling – education utopia!

However, as the days went on, my stomach was becoming ever more uncomfortable.

December 2017
Tuesday 12   The first tests

Finally, the date for the first tests arrived. I drove to Stoke Mandeville Hospital in a cheerful frame of mind, to have blood tests followed by an abdominal ultrasound scan. Both went without much fuss. I don't usually give blood away easily, but this time the nurse was successful at the first attempt. The scan was very gentle and simply involved the application of some jelly to the abdomen and then the guiding of a hand-held probe over the area to be investigated. All quite comfortable and unremarkable.

December 2017
Wednesday 13   Nothing much

A phone call from the local surgery revealed kidney cysts. Nothing serious they told me. Many people have these, and without a scan, most don't even know they have them. I felt a certain relief. But the stomach pain was getting worse. So I booked another appointment with Dr Noden.

December 2017
Tuesday 19   Bit of a misdiagnosis

It turned out it isn't kidney cysts after all, but liver cysts, along with some inflammation. Dr Noden said he'd look into this in more detail and ring me on Thursday.

December 2017
Thursday 21   The first scare

I had a visit to my dentist in London this afternoon followed immediately, with unfortunate timing, by tea with my great friend, Richard King, CEO of Faber Music (my publisher). Bad timing because after the dentist I could not express myself in anything but primordial grunts! Happily the anaesthetic began to wear off and, sometime between the scones and the patisserie, I had the anticipated phone call from Dr Noden. He told me he'd been looking more closely at the results so far and chatting with another doctor. He proposed an MRI (Magnetic Resonance Imaging) scan – more powerful than ultrasound – to check it wasn't pancreatic cancer. It was a scary call. And quite a leap from liver cysts. The MRI scan, also at Stoke Mandeville, was booked.

December 2017 *A day out in Manchester*
Wednesday 27 *and some difficult thoughts*

I had pancreatic cancer much in my mind today, whilst visiting my lovely friend Karen Marshall (writer of many piano teaching books) and her two delightful daughters, in Manchester. We visited the surprisingly unkempt Blue Peter Gardens and had a good laugh. But death was a constant thought. I don't fear death. But for me, the thought of *missing out* is indescribably frustrating. I love life, I love those close to me, I always want to know what's going on, I want to be at the party. Squaring up to that in my mind is extremely difficult. What is tomorrow going to bring?

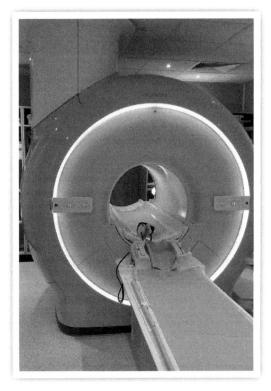

December 2017 *Big questions*
Thursday 28

Off to Stoke Mandeville again. So what *is* today going to bring? An MRI scan is a bit more of a procedure than an ultrasound. It took longer to set up and lasted around fifteen minutes. A bit noisy, but painless and not unpleasant.

In the afternoon I received a phone call from the surgery, saying they'd like to see me in about a week to discuss the results. The fact that they didn't want to see me immediately led me to believe it could be nothing too serious. Maybe things are not as bad as I had been thinking. But the stomach pain has been seriously increasing and I spent the night in absolute agony, curled and propped up on the sofa, as the painkillers prescribed by Dr Noden seemed to have little effect.

December 2017 *Serious developments*
Friday 29

8.00am

This morning I rang the surgery and asked if I could see a doctor as soon as possible. I explained that I'd spent the night in indescribable pain. They gave me an appointment right away and I had a few tests first with a nurse. The young lady doctor was studying the results of yesterday's scan with a rather concerned expression when I entered her consulting room. 'Right,' she announced a few moments later with a seriously determined exclamation, 'I'm sending you to the cancer unit at Stoke Mandeville Hospital immediately to have a stomach biopsy and to see a consultant.' It was the first time the word 'cancer' had been used in such a *direct* way. She rang the consultant and had quite a long conversation. I couldn't understand most it – it was as if she was speaking in a foreign language – all medical techno-speak. Then she printed out a letter for me to take to the hospital. The appointment was at midday. I set off straight away with a deep sense of foreboding.

11.30am

On arriving at Stoke Mandeville I searched for the Cancer and Haematology department. The very act of making my way there was extremely unsettling, especially as I was on my own. I entered a large waiting area where a number of people were sitting quietly and thoughtfully in rows of chairs, perhaps contemplating their own destiny.

I presented myself to the receptionist who was, as they often are, staring intently at a computer screen. I managed as cheerful a greeting as I could, in an attempt to prize her eyes from the computer: 'My GP has arranged an appointment for me at midday. Here's the letter she's given me ...' The lady looked back at her computer screen, 'I'm sorry but you're not on the system ...' 'What does that mean?' I enquired nervously. We went around in circles for a few minutes until she announced, 'Well, you'll just have to go home.' I was frustrated and annoyed by this time. The NHS was letting me down. No way was I going home. I began working out a strategy involving complicated phone calls to put this right, when a curious thing happened. A doctor had appeared a minute or so earlier and was busying himself in the receptionist area. He had overheard a certain amount of our conversation, and just as I was giving up hope and reaching for the phone, he said, 'Oh yes, this is my patient, I had that phone call earlier with his GP, it's fine, put him on the list.' Thank goodness for that, I thought. But, on this occasion, it would seem, things turned out okay through *pure luck* – surely this is not how it should work!

12.00pm

First, I had a 'rainbow' of blood tests. Meaning, an awful lot of blood was taken, to test in different ways. There's usually a certain amount of pain as the needle pierces the skin, especially if it takes three or four attempts to find a compliant vein – but I was getting used to it. I like the nurses who take blood as they're always chatty and cheerful. And I like to chat during the process too. I don't mind this procedure but I feel better talking away. Then there was a long wait while the blood was being analyzed. It's impossible to stop the mind from wandering into all kinds of unhappy thoughts in such a situation. And I had them all. From the worst scenario to more happy outcomes ... But then I made an important decision, to go with the flow and accept all thoughts, to neither deny them nor dismiss them. I've always loved the concept of flow – in relationships, in conversations, in teaching, in thinking, in all things. When you block (deliberately or unintentionally) or someone else blocks the flow, this can be both mentally and physically unhealthy. So, I accepted all thoughts, explored all possibilities, allowed them to inhabit my mind for a while – and then moved them on. I was not going to be trapped by negative thinking.

A charming young doctor then appeared and I was invited into his office for a chat. He asked many questions about my health history. I told him I'd never been ill before apart from the odd cold, a hernia, tonsillitis when I was a child and a rather curious experience of a hydrocele (a swelling in the scrotum) a few years ago. (This, at one point, involved a very attractive young lady doctor exploring my parts, whilst I attempted to internally compute the most complex mathematical sums I could come up with, in order to avoid any embarrassment.) I am, I told the doctor confidently, a fit and healthy person. I hardly drink, eat healthily, have never smoked and have always looked after myself carefully. We talked of my parents. My father died of leukaemia at a relatively young age and at the height of his very successful career as sales director for an American company that made the fibre tips for fibre tip pens. His leukaemia (Acute Myeloid Leukaemia or AML) could have been fixed now, but not then. My mother, always wonderfully stoic and warm-hearted, endured terrible health for years, but never complained. And we talked much about my present condition. The other consultant, Oliver, who I'd met at Reception earlier, then joined us. The two of them chatted for a while before I was brought back into the conversation. 'Well,' Oliver began, 'don't overly worry ... we don't feel the need to do the stomach biopsy today, but will book it in soon. You do have inflammation of the stomach lymph nodes; we'll be arranging a further series of tests now and we'll see you on January 24, when we should have a diagnosis for you.'

So at least I had some clear sense of direction now. I was being looked after by some top consultants at Stoke Mandeville, a world class hospital. I left the Cancer and Haematology department a little happier than I had arrived.

My parents

14

January 2018
Sunday 7 *Clarinets and stomachs*

This weekend I was coaching on a clarinet course along with two good friends, Shea Lolin and Anthony Bailey. We've done this for a few years now and it gets the year off to a very pleasant start. Benslow Music in Hitchin is an outstanding organization for continuing musical education, run by Peter Hewitt. It was my birthday today, too, so Anthony had the ensemble deliver a splendid rendition of the inescapable tune! I had to take my leave though, before the end of the course, to attend an appointment at Stoke Mandeville with a gastroenterologist. Maybe he could find an explanation for my continuing and debilitating stomach pain.

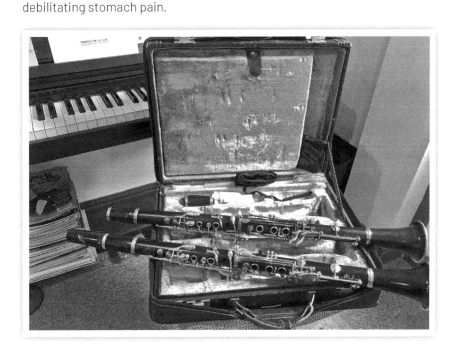

At first the doctor seemed rather uninterested in my case, until I told him about my trips to Dubai, India, South Africa and China, all reasonably recently ... could I have picked up a bug or a parasite, I enquired? Something that had remained dormant and suddenly sprung to life to cause havoc with my insides? It did the trick! It whetted his appetite and he agreed I should have an endoscopy.

January 2018
Tuesday 16 *Biopsy day*

Today the promised stomach biopsy finally arrived. Again I drove myself to Stoke Mandeville Hospital. The receptionists don't exactly show enthusiasm towards visitors, perhaps due to the often thankless nature of their work. The first trick was to get them to wrench their gazes from their computer screens. However, as I often find with pupils, they did seem to respond to humour and appreciation. I offered a little of the former and lots of the latter and so was sent off in the right direction with a smile. I was told to follow a helpful, if rather worn, red line painted on the floor, and soon arrived at the appropriate department. Most of the other patients in the waiting area (a nondescript corridor) were not looking especially happy or communicative, so I set about reading a book on education I'd brought with me, whilst waiting for my turn. It's not a very pleasant test, but in the hands of a good doctor, it's not especially uncomfortable. I don't like needles and caught a glimpse of some rather nasty-looking long syringes on a table. I averted my eyes instantly. For this the patient is not sedated but a local anaesthetic is applied. Entrance to the stomach is through the lower back. I had to do some deep breathing (being a clarinettist, something I'm good at) and keep very still. In fact, the doctor did the whole thing (taking three bits of tissue, I understood) without me really noticing. 'All done,' he announced, almost before I realized he'd begun.

January 2018
Monday 22   *Endoscopy day*

I was not especially looking forward to this appointment. But I felt it was very important in case it revealed that this whole thing *was* a parasitic growth, or maybe just a stomach or duodenal ulcer. Either would have been reasonably simple to cure. I've had a camera down my throat before – when a virus put one of my vocal chords out of action, whilst I was presenting music teaching workshops in Dubai a few years ago – so I knew what was coming.

The nurse who looked after me was lovely. She explained everything in minute detail in her small office and then, at the appropriate time, we walked down to the endoscopy room. The nurse indicated that I should sit on the side of the bed. The doctor who was to carry out the procedure was sitting with his back to us, at his computer, looking (I presumed) at my case notes. 'Good morning,' I offered, and under the circumstances, in a reasonably cheerful manner ... But there was no reply. I waited a few seconds, 'Morning,' I tried again, a little more assertively. Still no response. In a very loud stage whisper I turned to the nice nurse who was standing by my side and asked, 'Is he always like this?' 'Oh, he's usually very nice,' she responded, in a much more hushed whisper. This little exchange finally caused the good doctor to spin around, meet my eye and splutter a slightly reluctant greeting. He sported one of those full but wispy beards.

It's so important to have that contact. To make a connection. Most doctors I'd met so far, and many I was to meet later in this journey, were wonderfully good at communication. But the teacher in me was always going to make the point if they weren't. I was determined never to be thought of as an object. In most human interactions, transient or more permanent, making meaningful connection is essential, whether achieved through body language or facial gesture or empathetic conversation. Teachers, I've noticed, sometimes *forget that each of their pupils is a complex and fascinating **individual** – not merely just another pupil to be taught. The difference that can make in any developing relationship, short or long term, is very significant.*

1 *Do No Harm: Stories of Life, Death and Brain Surgery*, Henry Marsh (W&N, 2014)

Maybe things are different in some medical transactions. Maybe some doctors do need to view their patients dispassionately. Perhaps by objectivising them, they become easier to treat. But having read Henry Marsh's wonderful book on being a brain surgeon[1] I don't really believe this to be the case.

Of course, the doctor with the wispy beard carried out his work professionally and competently. I was given a small sedative so the procedure was not too unpleasant. The result was not ulcers or parasites, he told me, but serious gastritis and oesophagitis – which explained the extreme stomach-area pain I was enduring. There was clearly something else causing the problem, but not *in* the stomach. He suggested cancer.

January 2018
Wednesday 24   *Diagnosis day*

The day for the diagnosis had come. My lovely friend Helen who I've known since the age of about nine, daughter of my great mentor and teacher John Davies, had agreed to join me for this meeting. We met one of the senior consultants (who also, coincidentally, was called Helen) in the large waiting area of the Cancer and Haematology department at Stoke Mandeville Hospital. After a while I was ushered off to have some more blood taken. I recognized the nurse – she had taken some of my blood before – and we had a lively chat during the process. Then more waiting, before finally we were invited into Consultant Helen's office. She had me lie on her couch and felt around a bit. Then I sat down opposite her and her expression became very serious. 'I have some rather bleak news for you,' she announced with a kind of Shakespearean gravity. I felt I knew what was coming and inwardly would have rather she delivered it in a slightly less weighty manner. 'You have high-grade, diffuse, non-Hodgkin lymphoma (NHL),' she announced. 'It's a cancer of the blood that affects the lymph system, which is basically the immune system. The survival rate is between sixty and seventy percent.' Not exactly a cheerful statistic. Jackie Kennedy and Paul Allen (co-founder of Microsoft) are among the great many who have died from NHL. And furthermore, if the treatment doesn't work first time, there's no more to be done. We were there for about an hour, while she explained a lot more than I took in. It was also the first time the word 'tumour' was mentioned. It's a scary word. But I was determined from the outset that this unwelcome visitor was only going to have temporary residence. I was determined to survive.

Consultant Helen then gave us a book about lymphoma and introduced us to a nurse who would be my main contact through the whole long process to follow. She also mentioned something else that was ultimately to change the direction of the next period of my life. 'We have a meeting of all the top lymphoma consultants here today and I've a feeling one might be interested in your case … we'll let you know later this afternoon.'

True to her word and her assumption, as Helen was driving me home, Consultant Helen rang and said a Dr Graham Collins *was* interested in my case and would like to see me at nine o'clock on Monday morning at the Lymphoma Unit at The Churchill Hospital in Oxford.

January 2018
Monday 29 *A new direction?*

Naturally I googled Dr Collins MA MBBS MRCP FRCPath DPhil and he seemed to be a top man in the field. But to become a patient of his I had to pass a series of tests.

Another wonderful friend, Jean, came with me to this meeting. It's so important to have someone with you at such meetings. Besides anything else, they can take in all the stuff that you can't (which is most of it!). The very affable Graham Collins explained he was running a trial based on a new drug (on top of the conventional treatment) and I would have to go through two days of tests in order to find out whether I was eligible or not. I agreed enthusiastically. So I was booked in at The Churchill for the next two days.

Also today, I met the nurse who would become my guardian angel if I passed the tests – Emma Scott. My main point of contact at any time. Emma greeted me as if she'd known me all my life, with a wonderfully instinctive sense of empathy and kindness. Fingers crossed.

January 2018
Tuesday 30 *Tests*

I checked in with Emma and the day began with a meeting with 'Doctor P' in the Early Phase Clinical Trials Unit (EPCTU). We had a long chat and he explained all the tests I was about to go through over the next two days, to see if I was indeed going to be eligible for this trial. I have to say, and this thought was continually strengthened and deepened as the days and weeks advanced, that the bedside manner of virtually all the doctors and nurses I met was exemplary. However, 'Doctor P' had a little to learn here. Empathy is such an important quality – maybe *the* most important quality for medics and teachers alike. Being a teacher, I did, maybe slightly presumptuously, make a passing comment to him about his own slightly wanting bedside manner. He talked *at* me rather than *with* me. He didn't make me feel comfortable. Not sure that my comment hit the mark or even whether I should have mentioned it. But there we are, once a teacher, always a teacher.

The first test was a bone marrow biopsy. These I don't recommend. I couldn't be given any sedation (this would evidently require another nurse in attendance), so it was done just with local anaesthetic. They drill into the pelvic bone and you can both hear and feel it. But it was bearable. Then there were lots of blood tests. In the afternoon, the main test was a PET (Positron Emission Tomography) scan, carried out in one of those big, tunnel-like machines. It was a long, thirty-minute-or-so procedure, very noisy and you become radioactive for a while (so no mixing with pregnant women for a few hours afterwards I was told – I assured the doctor that this was unlikely). But, bar having to hold your hands and arms above your head for a long time, it's not uncomfortable.

January 2018
Wednesday 31   More tests

I had flu and pneumonia jabs today, plus an ECG, and a complicated heart scan which took nearly an hour. But nothing unpleasant. They said I'd hear by the end of the week whether I had passed the tests and was therefore eligible for the new treatment. I didn't hear and felt very despondent. It didn't look promising.

February 2018
Monday 5   Results

I did finally hear today and the news was good. I was eligible for the trial! The first chemotherapy treatment would be this very Wednesday. I knew I was going to be in good hands. I rang Stoke Mandeville Hospital and explained that my treatment would now be taking place in Oxford. They were very supportive.

February 2018
Tuesday 6   Another (brief) intermission

This would turn out to be my last day of 'outside' work for a good long while. My High-grade non-Hodgkin diffuse large B-cell lymphoma (stage IIIb) is a cancer of the immune system and, as such, means I would have to be very careful about catching infections – I'd have no way to fight them. So for the coming months, public places were to be out of bounds. But I was determined to make this particular engagement work and drove over to Bedford Modern

School with great anticipation. I was delighted to be adjudicating their music performance prizes. Especially so as Alan Taylor, Director of Music from my highly enjoyable days as a pupil at Haberdashers' Aske's School, was himself a pupil at Bedford Modern. I was much looking forward to telling Alan all about it when I got home in the evening. It was a lovely day. Great music-making at all levels by the really enthusiastic and engaged young musicians under the inspired directorship of John Mower.

February 2018
Wednesday 7   *Chemo 1*

8.00am

I was ensconced in a pleasant single room and the day began by way of a chat with a doctor and the taking of a lot of blood. I then had a permanent PICC line (Peripherally Inserted Central Catheter) fitted to my upper left arm – I particularly asked for the left arm to allow me to conduct, just in case the unlikely opportunity arose in these next few months. Having a PICC line means chemicals can be injected or blood taken without having to set up a new point of entry each time. In my case, as a musician, this was very important. Often, they inject through the wrist and this can cause complications. PICC lines can stay fitted for up to eighteen months, I understand. It was the excellent Liz who fitted it. We chatted the whole time and it turned out she was looking for

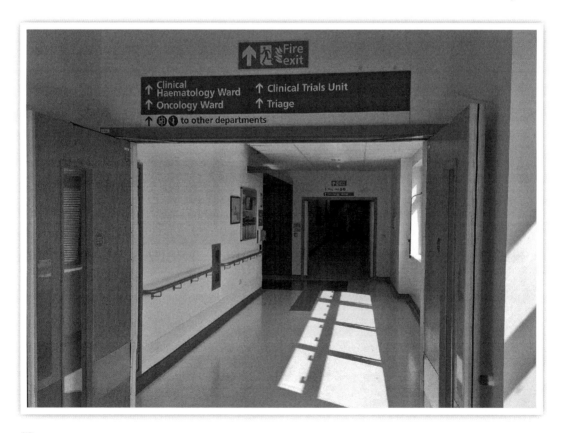

a guitar teacher for both herself and her five-and-a-half-year-old son. I was delighted to hear this and told her I would do my best to find a teacher for her – happily I did. Then a wait to see that the blood taken revealed I was okay to receive the first batch of chemicals. It was.

2 https://www.macmillan.org.uk/information-and-support/treating/chemotherapy/drugs-and-combination-regimens/combination-chemotherapy/r-chop.html

The basic cocktail of chemicals for this cancer is called R-CHOP[2], standing for:
- R – Rituximab
- C – Cyclophosphamide
- H – Hydroxydaunomycin or doxorubicin
- O – Oncovin or vincristine
- P – Prednisolone (a steroid)

Some of the drugs are injected via enormous syringes. As for those that take longer, I was hooked up to a drip, and in the stuff goes. I was originally told it would take a few hours – in fact it took seven and a half. It really was mentally overwhelming. It was on this first chemo day that the whole thing really hit me. I had brought books and my computer, but was unable to make use of either.

And as I lay on the bed for all those hours I became acutely aware of the continual rhythmic beeping and alarms emanating from all the various devices attached to patients – indicating a fall in blood pressure, a pump malfunction, a blockage in the tubing as chemicals were being injected, or maybe an empty medication bag. It sounded like a kind of strange and mildly terrifying electronic aviary, or a work of extreme counterpoint by John Adams. Nurses respond, but often not immediately, and the cacophony can become quite exasperating.

5.10pm

My stalwart friend Tony Meredith (author of such diverse books as a biography of W. G. Grace, the histories of Silverstone and Northampton, and co-biographer – with me – of the great composer Malcolm Arnold) had brought me to hospital first thing this morning and then arrived to pick me up. There were still quite a lot of chemicals to be injected and so Tony sat with me as the final ninety minutes dragged by. We used the time to make up a timetable for the innumerable, suitcase-full of drugs I'd been given, to be taken at home every day for the duration of the treatment.

February 2018
Thursday 8   Sledgehammers and music of the spheres

That first chemo hit me like a sledgehammer. I was exhausted today and felt very weak. The chemo drugs have all sorts of side effects. Some hit immediately, others emerge over time. In my case the first to become apparent was certain bodily functions that stopped working properly i.e. the passing of liquids and solids. It all gets very frustrating and unpleasant. I had medicines from Dr Noden, but nothing seemed to make much difference. Not happy times.

I also had a most curious experience. I began to hear music – a mixture of bells and panpipe-like sounds. I thought I'd left a device on somewhere in the house and checked each of them – none were on. Then I realized what it was. The two lumens – the name they give to the external plugs connected to my PICC line – were responsible. The sounds were literally coming out of my body and these lumens were acting like amplifiers – ethereal music of the inner spheres. Extraordinary.

February 2018
Friday 9   Cabin fever

My mind began racing today – I became impatient, frustrated, and couldn't focus. This new life of incarceration and isolation – so contrasting with my former dynamic existence – was beginning to have a bad effect. I thought I might need the help of a clinical psychologist. It was driving me mad. To an extent, one's work is one's identity – and I feel that I'm losing mine. Stuck at home all the time with the thought of the many similar months ahead is truly exasperating. I've never had to consciously fill time before, there was always something in the diary. I'm going to have to learn just to 'be' – and to be satisfied with that. This is going to take a lot of careful thought to manage.

February 2018
Sunday 11   Cabin fever II

I decided to hold fire on seeing anyone about this problem after a very useful conversation with an empathetic friend of a friend, a cancer survivor. He told me to concentrate on three areas outside the whole medical arena – mental approach (totally positive), good diet (doing my best, though been struggling with appetite for quite a while) and exercise. I did consider these much more carefully and thankfully the cabin fever began to recede.

February 2018
Tuesday 13   Thoughts that require processing

The 'Why me?' question popped into my mind today. Not sure why. But I decided it was probably better to deal with it up front, rather than for it to stay repressed in the subconscious. On the whole, they say, cancer is not the result of lifestyle; it's rarely caused by the environment and is also rarely genetic. I had thought that maybe my father was responsible (having died from leukaemia), but I was told firmly otherwise by a trustworthy doctor. In two out of three cases, generally speaking, it's just bad luck. A cell mutates, the body's immune system can't deal with it, and cancer ensues. I have no intention of feeling sorry for myself, or playing the victim. I can't see any point in that at all. By not playing the victim one is driven towards being more positively resourceful, which I'm sure is a good thing. And I don't want people to feel sorry for me – it's their support I need.

February 2018
Friday 16   Sickness I

Tony took me out for a drive to an antiques emporium in Bicester this morning, for a bit of retail therapy. I wanted to buy something for my garden and this particular centre sells all manner of surprising curiosities. I liked a tall and very colourful totem pole which I thought would look rather impressive in my garden, but it was a little too expensive; disappointingly my powers of haggling fell on deaf ears. On the way back, embarrassingly, I was sick in Tony's car. Luckily, I had brought precautionary measures with me (thick towels) so managed to be as discreet as possible. I was sick again later. Another unpleasant side effect.

February 2018
Saturday 17 to Sunday 18   Sickness II

I felt sick again this morning. Feeling sick is one of the 'ring-the-hospital-straight-away criteria' – I have a list of them in a useful little handbook I was given. So I did, and was invited in immediately. Lots of blood samples were taken and lots of pills swallowed. I was kept in overnight but allowed home late afternoon on Sunday. This was probably the beginning of an infection that was really about to come into its own.

February 2018
Monday 19   Constipation

One (or more) of the chemotherapy drugs is responsible for the rather unpleasant side effect of constipation. And that was today's nadir. A long and very difficult session in the small room. Without overstating the situation,

I think I can truly say it was the most painful experience I've ever encountered. Having had no bowel movements for a couple of days, what eventually passed through was very large, very hard and very agonizing.

February 2018
Tuesday 20   *A bad day*

I woke up feeling weak and cold so raised the house thermostat to 23 degrees. Fortunately it was a 'Jenny morning' – Jenny is my PA, and a loyal friend. Temperature-taking was something I was doing regularly and as I felt particularly unwell this morning, I decided to see what it was. It was sky high – 38.5 or .6 in the other ear. I rang the hospital – another rule is anything above 37.5 and you ring immediately. The nurse on the other end of the telephone asked me to make a beeline for the hospital. I gathered together the barest minimum of overnight stuff (just in case), and Jenny drove me over to Oxford.

The first thing that usually happens when I arrive is that I am weighed. I was seriously distressed to find that my weight had decreased significantly to below ten stone (it is normally about thirteen). Then they took a lot of blood. Maybe eight or nine phials. The nurse had to go and get more phials during the procedure. Not long afterwards I was attached to an intravenous antibiotic drip. I felt really ill. I did in fact have Neutropenic Sepsis – an abnormally low level of neutrophils or white blood cells that are essential to fighting off infections. I was given injections into my stomach (not as bad as it sounds, by the way). I later learned that my neutrophil count was very low, at 0.02 (between 3.5 and 10 is normal).

I ended up staying in hospital for the rest of the week. I began to feel better and made friends with a particular kind of very high-calorie drink. I had at least three of these a day, which added up to about a thousand calories. Plus, at 10.30 in the morning and 3.30 in the afternoon, the wonderfully smiley 'Milkshake Magda' brought around the sort of drink I wouldn't normally have touched. Rich chocolate and vanilla milkshakes. Delicious. I'd often have two at a time! Even more calories. I was determined to do something about my pitiful weight. And as the week progressed, I gradually felt stronger and did my best to eat as much of the dreadful hospital food as I could. Hospital food really is ghastly! Potatoes that aren't properly cooked, lentil pie that tasted truly horrible, sponge pudding that had the consistency of a house brick ... But it's always served nicely, albeit at extraordinary times (lunch as early as 11.45am and supper at 5.00pm!).

I spent the days thinking, having tests, reading and watching rather a lot of TV on my computer.

February 2018
Wednesday 21
A transformative thought and a difficult decision

2am

I had a powerful and transformative experience very early this morning. About 2am I awoke with some considerable tenderness and aching in my external anal sphincter area – the result of the constipation. I was worried that it might be infected and that this was why I was in hospital. What to do? At first I felt uncomfortable about asking the night nurse to come and take a look. I've never been at all prudish but this was a difficult call. But I thought about it, and decided to think myself into the medical world. To me, a parallel universe. But medics of course think nothing of such a request. It's what they do. It made a huge difference. I pressed the red button and heard a buzzer sound at the night nurse's desk. She arrived moments later. As usual it was a young lady nurse, but my mind was altered. This is what she does. This is simply routine. She had a look and put my mind at rest. A little inflamed but nothing to worry about.

*There was not much chance of sleep for a bit so I thought long and hard about how this mental leap might be applied to teaching. And I realized that as teachers we have to think ourselves, as best we can, into our pupils' worlds. Our level of empathy has to become very high. I often talk about empathy as a quality of the 'Virtuoso Teacher'[3]. But I suddenly knew that I need to make much more of it. The degree and understanding of empathy needs to be very acute. What are our pupils thinking, feeling? How are they really responding and reacting to **our** responses, and our reactions to them? How aligned are our two worlds? It seems to me that there are countless parallel universes, many of which we need to try to understand. Other peoples' lives are more different than we may think. My life is largely made up of teachers and pupils; clarinettists and pianists and other musicians; and now, added to those wonderful people, medics are playing a major part. Each of these individual's own universe is much more discrete than we might imagine. The attempt to enter them is a major step forward in understanding other people. And it will have a major impact on our ability to communicate effectively. This is what empathy is all about. I'm not sure you can really teach empathy – but you can make people aware of it. Then they have to work it out for themselves. (Regrettably, there are some for whom it simply will not resonate. I hope those particular people don't become teachers.)*

3 *The Virtuoso Teacher*, Paul Harris (Faber Music, 2012)

25

9am

A doctor always pops in around nine o'clock. I told him about my incident in the middle of the night and that it now felt like I was continuously sitting on a ping pong ball. He told me he'd send another doctor to have a look sometime during the day. After my transformative experience last night, I was completely at ease with doctors looking wherever they need to. It was another young lady doctor who arrived just before lunch and told me I had an anal fissure (a tear in the anal lining) caused by the constipation on Monday. Very painful at the moment, but it would clear up in time.

I watched the complete eight episodes of a TV series about serious organised crime called *McMafia* today. Much enjoyed it and was quite amazed to find it was based on a true story. There is such corruption in the world. I'm becoming quite the couch potato (or maybe bed potato, in my case).

February 2018
Thursday 22   *Departure*

Was released from hospital today. It's been quite a momentous stay.

February 2018
Sunday 25   *Wait for weight*

Slept well for a change and woke up feeling energetic. The first thought that popped into my mind was my weight, so decided to find out whether a few days of more enthusiastic eating had made any effect. I was delighted to find that I had edged just over ten stone. Those high-calorie drinks are making a difference.

February 2018
Wednesday 28   *Chemo 2 and a careless moment*

We're in the middle of the 'Beast from the East' at the moment. This is the rather poetic label given to some really bad wintry weather that's come over from Siberia. So, I indulged myself in an overnight stay at the excellent Macdonald Randolph Hotel in Oxford last night, just in case snow might have impeded my journey from Buckingham. It's my second chemo today and I don't want to jeopardize that in any way.

My love of Inspector Morse (many scenes are set in or near the Randolph and it has its own 'Morse Bar') was the main factor in choosing that particular hotel. I had a very spacious room with all the trimmings and the plan worked. I arrived at The Churchill in very good time. But I had had some marmalade on my breakfast toast! There are only two restrictions to the foods you can eat alongside this particular chemotherapy cocktail – oranges and grapefruit.

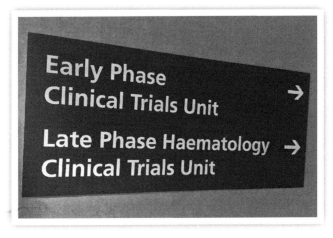

They both interfere with efficacy of the drugs. Marmalade and oranges – I hadn't made the connection. It was to cause something of a problem a little later this morning.

I was greeted by the wonderful Emma, my guardian angel, in her inimitably warm and caring manner. Ellie, another terrific nurse who I also liked enormously, took what seemed literally like pints of blood on arrival. She must have filled up about fifteen phials of it. Then all the other 'obs' were performed: blood pressure, pulse, temperature and breathing rate, among others. And I was to have a blood sample taken every two hours today, until 6.30pm.

I'm not sure how it emerged, but my marmalade moment was revealed. And it almost put paid to today's chemo. After the trouble I had taken, that would have been a blow. Thankfully it was decided (after quite some debate and deliberation) that my one piece of toast, on which (I assured them) I had spread only the slenderest coating of the preserve, wasn't going to represent a risk. So on with the long wait for the blood results during which time another doctor I was getting to know well – with an appropriate nickname (for me, anyway) of 'Mus' – came to see me. Mus is Australian, very outgoing and friendly. I brought him up to date and asked lots of questions. He seemed pleased with progress generally.

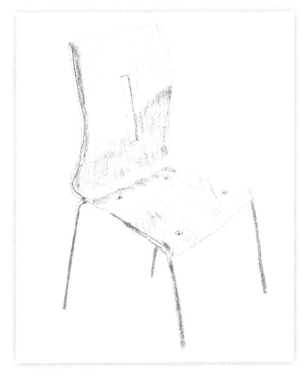

About midday, nurses Emma and Dot came to prepare me for today's infusion. It went much as last time, but I was much more psychologically prepared and it only lasted five hours this time. Jean had brought me some drawing materials and so I did some sketching. I've always loved the idea of being able to draw a bit. My results leave an awful lot to be desired but it's very engaging and certainly helps pass the time in an agreeably creative way. I had also been speaking to Dot earlier and it turned out that her daughter really wanted an internship with a publisher. Right up my street, I told Dot, and during the treatment I was able to make some phone calls and set this up for her. Nice to still feel useful.

Julia, another great friend from nearby, popped in and brought some delicious celery soup. (The hospital did provide a rather sickly and unappetising egg mayonnaise sandwich, but I managed only a couple of mouthfuls before giving up the attempt.)

It was all over by 6.30pm as planned. Hayley changed my PICC line dressing and I was allowed home. Jenny picked me up and I was back by 8pm. A long and exhausting day, but much more of a controlled experience compared with the first.

March 2018
Friday 2 More side effects

The first week, post chemo 2, is going okay. I'm feeling stronger by day, but not sleeping well. A particularly annoying side effect is poor functioning of the waterworks and I guess I need to go about ten or more times during the course of a night, which interrupts the already poor quality of sleep. My GP has got into the generous and very caring habit of calling me every Thursday afternoon for a quick catch-up and I shall certainly ask him about this on his next call. Another curious side effect is an unpleasant metallic taste. Almost everything has a rather bitter flavour and none of my usually favourite foods are presently palatable. Because my stomach itself is pretty much back to normal, I gingerly tried a supermarket curry this evening (usually one of my favourite foods) – it went down okay but tasted disagreeable. Oh well, just something else to put up with for the time being.

March 2018
Sunday 4 Friends and yet more side effects

4 I run a weekend-long festival in Northampton every year to celebrate the music of this great British composer.

Visitors and telephone conversations are my lifeline whilst not being able to go out and mix in (potentially infected) company for the next few months. So today was going to be fun with an early visit from Jonathan, who helps me reply to my fifty-or-so a day emails, sorts my social media and is my right-hand man in organising the Malcolm Arnold Festival[4].

My great friends Helen and Richard then arrived with some much-appreciated lunch. Richard is chairman of a major British university and was formerly chair of Faber Music (among many other things,) so we had lots to talk about. The chicken, happily, was not corrupted by my normally disobliging taste buds and I actually enjoyed it. Now that the snow has largely disappeared we were also able to go for a decent walk, which I hugely enjoyed. Of the three additional, non-medical, supporting 'treatments' – positive attitude, good food and exercise – the last has been rather neglected. A good time to make amends. And I had a third visitor, too – my delightful pupil Georgina. When possible, I've been continuing to give lessons since chemo began – pupils providing so much pleasure. And Georgina (herself a very talented artist as well as outstanding clarinettist) has also been encouraging me to sketch – a growing pleasure and pastime in this new daily life-style I'm having to fashion.

The evening wasn't so much fun. Regulating constipation requires so much care. One has to monitor what's happening so meticulously. Very little signs of number twos – but no shortage of number ones. One of the chemo drugs causes one to go with considerable regularity, and endless times at night. So I decided on a double dose of Laxido and a Senna tablet and hoped I'd timed it well. I couldn't bear a repeat of former experiences. I think I got it right.

5 http://
scienceblog.
cancerresearchuk.
org/2014/08/27/
mustard-gas-
from-the-great-
war-to-frontline-
chemotherapy

March 2018
Tuesday 6 *Some history, some weakness and some strength*

I discovered today, from Ellen, one of my adult pupils who came for a lesson this morning, that one of the drugs in the R-CHOP cocktail, Cyclophosphamide, is actually Mustard Gas – in other words, a constituent part of first-world-war biological weaponry. There's a very interesting website that shows its development from villain to hero[5].

Felt very weak in the afternoon – but managed some proof-reading. It was the final proofs of both Clarinet and Flute *Improve Your Scales*, Grades 1–3. Over the years I've written many of these books, and of course proof-read them too. But the excitement never recedes; a new book, even a new edition of an existing book is exhilarating and enlivening. And the desire to keep improving them – both in content and in presentation, is always there. I've always been grateful that my mind works like that – but then that's the way it should be.

In writing, in playing, in teaching, we should always be striving to seek new routes and new solutions. Especially in things we've done before, perhaps a great many times, where it can so easily become a chore – and with a little imagination it's interesting to find that it always **is** *possible to discover alternatives.*

March 2018
Wednesday 7 *More tests and an unhappy patient*

Back in hospital today for tests. Tony picked me up at 6.30am and we set off on a journey with which we're now getting rather familiar. Into Oxford, just north of Summertown, around the ring road and then through Headington, past Headington School and Oxford Brookes University, The Churchill is then just up the road. Happily, arriving so early means there is always somewhere close to the entrance to park. A short walk takes us to the café for a quick coffee before I make my way up a many-stepped staircase to the first floor, turn left along a long corridor (there are *so* many long corridors in hospitals – actually I quite

like long corridors, as long as there are interesting people to pass and things to look at on the walls) and then left again into the EPCTU. The lovely Monica from Poland began by taking a lot of blood and then she cleared out a defective lumen in my PICC line. I hate to feel any parts of me (even extraneous, fixed-on parts for the time being) are not operating. Was very pleased to see that

my weight had gone up to ten stone two pounds – definitely a move in the right direction. I always chatter to the nurses – it's fascinating to catch a little of their life story each time we meet. And I think they appreciate being appreciated – they're all *very* special people.

Mus from Oz came to see me after another very unappetising excuse for 'lunch'. We talked a bit about my poor sleeping patterns and far too regular visits to the small room during the night. So, a urine sample was in order of the afternoon, in case of infection or inflammation. In return I mentioned, light-heartedly, his questionable posture as he sits at his desk (he's almost supine). Mus took my quip cheerfully and if I'm in again tomorrow we agreed I'd give him one of my posture routines with which I begin every lesson.

I was put in a small (three-person) ward today. One of my fellow patients was a retired bus driver who seemed in surprisingly good spirits. He was chatting about regularly going out for meals and there not being much interruption to his normal life style. Must be a very different cancer to mine. But the other patient was not happy. He was receiving some treatment through a drip and clearly not in a good way; shivering and sounding dour. Inevitably I caught a conversation with a nurse in which he told her his temperature often shoots up far higher than the tipping point where you're supposed to phone the hospital. 'It usually goes down eventually,' he said. The nurse gently suggested that he ought to call in anyway. He seemed to dismiss her advice and continued to suffer unhappily. Curious how some people refuse to abide by 'the rules'. I don't see there's any question, myself. In cases like these, playing by the rules is a necessity. Perhaps some people feel that they want to hang on to their independence by continuing to make their own choices. In the case of severe illness, it's probably better to hang on to it in other ways.

March 2018
Thursday 8   *Even more tests and the wonders of friendship*

Back in hospital for yet more tests. This meant leaving at 6.30am yet again, which, after a poor night's sleep, is not exactly a pleasure. Tony drove me in again and we arrived at 7.30am. There's a rather nice grand piano in the café area, on which sits a sign inviting those who could, to indulge in a little entertainment. I decided I'd give it a go today, so played the assembled crowd (quite a large one, in fact) some Bach. I was amused to get absolutely no reaction at all to my performance!

On having my weight measured first thing, I was disappointed to find that I'd slipped below ten stone again. I couldn't have lost three pounds overnight. Just demonstrates that not all NHS equipment is infallible. Oh well – lots more of those high-calorie drinks required.

11.30am

Having blood taken literally every 15 minutes at the moment. So drinking lots of water to replenish the blood. Actually I've no idea how blood is formed, but it must be something to do with bodily fluids, so drinking water must help!

Had a long chat with another patient. I hadn't met him before. A chap in his early forties maybe, with a young son. He told me that his cancer had spread quite seriously before treatment had begun. He seemed extremely stoic and philosophical about it. The future was very uncertain. These conversations are not easy; one can do little more than listen and empathize. There's no need to say very much. But such a conversation forms a powerful bond. I wished him good luck, wondered how his son was coping, and whether we would meet again.

Evening

My friend Esther picked me up and I was home by 5.00pm. It was a mixed evening. I have to have a stomach injection every evening (Jenny usually administers these) to avert neutropenia again. But it didn't quite work this evening, something seemed to go wrong with the syringe, so we had to ring the hospital mid-way through the process for advice. Not at all pleasant. And my waterworks were functioning very poorly. Also not pleasant.

But I had about three hours of phone calls from friends. You certainly get to know your real friends in times like these and I'm blessed with a fantastic group of close friends.

Other friends, some of whom one may have thought of as being close, seem to struggle to deal with cancer (even when it's not their own) and disappear. It's interesting how some people are so self-absorbed that they see life only through the prism of their own personal experience. Nothing wrong with that, but it does mitigate against empathy. Some friends struggle with what to say. In fact, I have found that maintaining normal conversation, accepting all the circumstances, is best. And I find it good to be absolutely open about all aspects. Even the more personal ones. It is surprising how easily close friends accept this and that makes for more natural and easy-going chatter. They're not worried about what or what not to say.

Cor anglais and a major drama

6 A woodwind instrument belonging to the oboe family.

A couple of months ago another wonderful friend, Melanie, commissioned me to write a set of cor anglais[6] pieces for a special event at The Purcell School (London's specialist music school). The event was instigated by Howarth of London Ltd (a specialist oboe maker and shop) to launch their new cor anglais designed for smaller hands. I wrote *Six Shakespeare Pieces*, one for each of Mel's Purcell pupils, and the event was today. Jill Crowther, principal cor anglais in the Philharmonia Orchestra, gave a masterclass on my pieces, which were then performed. I really would have loved to have been there but sadly I was not able to attend, though I hear it was a great success. Dealing with frustration is something else I've learnt to do during this whole process. I sent Mel a short, recorded message to be played at the event, and I had a phone call with all the participants during the course of the afternoon. With a little imagination I was still able to connect, even from a distance.

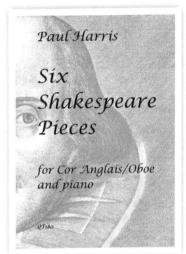

Paul Harris

Six Shakespeare Pieces

for Cor Anglais/Oboe and piano

QT180

3.30pm

Unfortunately had another one of those agonizing constipated bowel movements. I thought I was regulating this better – with all these various potions and pills. But clearly not. The pain at the point of exit became more and more intense as the afternoon, evening and night wore on.

11.30pm

By this time, I was in excruciating pain. I rang The Churchill and spoke to the haematology registrar who was helpful and reassured me that the cocktail of painkillers and constipation medicine I'd been taking should control it. It didn't. I rang Jenny and she came round, just before midnight, to support me. I was also shivering violently and uncontrollably. I have never felt so ill.

3.50am

I simply could not find any position, lying, sitting, or standing, that would relieve the pain. It was basically around the sphincter area and the gruesome death of Edward II came into my mind. The mental stress was also enormous. Hours of pain. I was telling myself it wouldn't last forever, that the pain was bearable. But it really wasn't. At about 4.00am I felt hot and took my temperature. It was 38.2, so I rang the Churchill. I was told to make a beeline for the A&E department at a local hospital. The registrar from The Churchill would ring and put them in the picture. Jenny and I, plus a very modest overnight bag, set off on a most uncomfortable journey about 5.00am.

5.30am

Arrived at A&E speedily, and after introducing myself was immediately taken off to another wing of the hospital and installed in a small room. Blood was taken as usual and various other tests including an ECG and a chest X-ray to check if I had pneumonia (I didn't). The staff were lovely. I was wheeled to X-ray, sitting crossed-legged on one of those bed trolleys, by the excellent Sean who had been wheeling patients on trolleys round the hospital for over twenty years – his skill was palpable, from getting around tight corners to sliding with effortless ease into lifts. We sailed from my room to the X-ray department and joined a queue lined up in the corridor. Finally, a journey I really enjoyed!

March 2018
Saturday 10   *A shambles and some wonderful friends*

Another fun, longer journey on Sean's bed trolley to Ward 23, Room 3 which would be my home for the next four days. Here I met the excellent Doctor Drew (born in Northern Ireland, brought up in Botswana) and Nurse Mildrew (not her real name) whose approach had all the finesse of a sledgehammer. She was responsible for my first ever suppository, which was delivered with 'brace yourself Paul, because I'm going to pack a real punch here.' Given the extreme sensitivity of this area, Mildrew's tactic was not that much appreciated. She

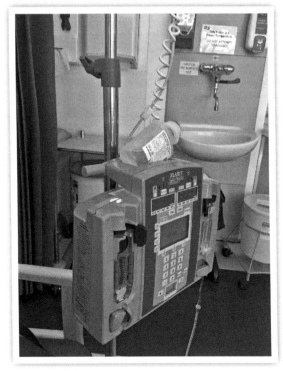

also gave me an unusually painful injection. When she started to fit a cannula, I said enough was enough, and asked her to find someone else. Again, the teacher in me was not going to stay silent. 'I need to teach you a new word', I told her at one point, 'gentleness.' She seemed surprised. I'm afraid to say that fitting a cannula to my right arm (the left already accommodating my PICC line) turned into the kind of shambles that does occasionally earn the NHS a less-than-perfect reputation.

First of all, a doctor called Sally (also not her real name) came along and fitted the cannula in about ninety seconds, close to my wrist. It was necessary for the blood transfusion I was about to have because of the severe infection I had developed. Then the good Mildrew and another nurse

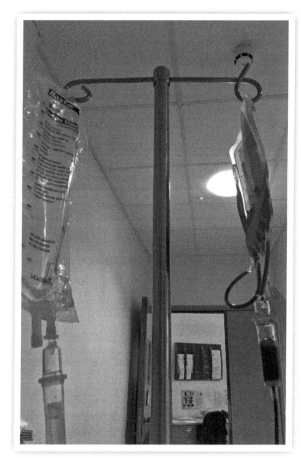

called Helen appeared. They fiddled with it, trying to connect it up, and finally decided it didn't work. There was quite a bit of discomfort during this process. I think they broke it. So Helen then fitted a second cannula further up my arm (not removing the first one, by the way) aided, as she did so, by random and confusing comments from Mildrew and yet another nurse who suddenly appeared but didn't seem to want to get involved (except in an advisory capacity). It had all the makings of a farce. Eventually they got it installed and, for about the next four hours, I had my blood transfusion. This was in addition to another drip that was flowing into my left arm. I think I really was quite ill at this time.

Dear Mel paid me a totally unexpected visit in the afternoon, as did my good friend, the piano supremo Andrew Eales, who lives not far away. They witnessed much of the above-mentioned shambles! Despite it all we had an enjoyable and entertaining afternoon. Night eventually came and I had to sleep with yet another drip attached to my left arm. Though regularly interrupted by the drip setting off an alarm each time I moved, I slept reasonably well and partially made up for the devastating previous night.

March 2018
Sunday 11 *Jam, spies and a famous house*

Almost nothing happened today. It was as if the hospital had virtually shut down. I had no blood tests (or any tests, for that matter) and no doctor came to see me. I somehow managed another day of hospital food. At least I was able to find their menu entertaining. I suppose someone somewhere might choose 'jam sandwich' from their (fairly unappetising) list of Sunday lunch main courses!

I hugely appreciated a visit from Tony in the afternoon which broke the monotony of the day. He brought me books on the composers Peter Maxwell Davies, Alan Rawsthorne and Elizabeth Poston – all of which I devoured with much enthusiasm. As well as being a composer, Elizabeth Poston was a spy. She used music to send messages to soldiers in France during World War

Two. But she never revealed how. She also lived in a house called Rooks Nest Cottage – later bought by composer and former Master of the Queen's music, Malcolm Williamson, and previously lived in by the great writer E. M. Forster and used as the model for *Howard's End*.

March 2018
Monday 12   *Some amazing new people*

8.50am

My bed was made this morning by Amelia, who sported a major tattoo on her right arm. She made the bed with more care and artistry than I've yet experienced. Including hospital corners. 'In the old days, the sister would have made us begin again if we didn't make the beds properly,' she told me, 'times have changed, but I still follow the old traditions.' Good to meet someone like Amelia who takes such pride in what she does.

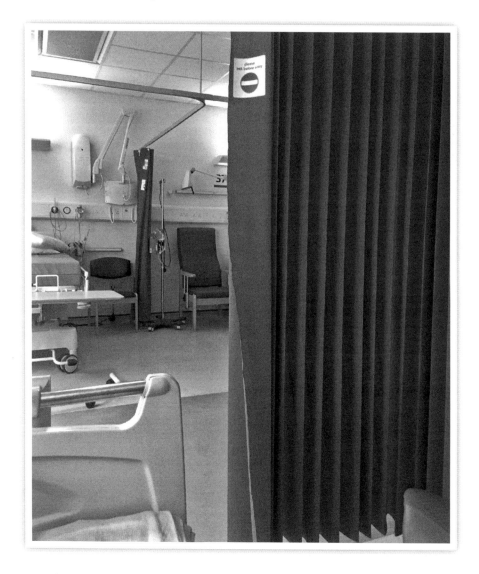

10.40am

Just had my blood taken by the delightful Angela, the phlebotomist. Wearing a smart green outfit, she introduced herself as Dracula and removed three phials of blood from me in the most pain-free, professional and funny manner. The number of times I've had blood taken, and finally I know that those who take it are called phlebotomists! The word comes from the Greek 'phleb' meaning vein, and 'tomia' meaning cut – so, literally, 'cutting a vein'.

Listened to all the Khachaturian Symphonies this morning between visits from assorted doctors and registrars. No. 1 is a practice, No. 2 is a masterpiece and No. 3 is an appalling piece of bombast, but I still love it! The news is mostly good – blood count going up but immunity still very low. Nevertheless, hoping to be sent home tomorrow.

Jean came to visit this afternoon. There's a very deep rack of bed pans outside my room and we noticed a ball sitting on a table. Jean suggested a game of tennis in the day room using the bed pans as rackets. I love Jean's rambunctious sense of the ridiculous! We didn't actually get around to the match owing to a walk over to the hospital's coffee shop. But it afforded a lot of very welcome laughter.

March 2018
Tuesday 13 *An alarming incident*

10.30am

Still here. The fire alarm went off. I sat on my bed awaiting developments. After about a minute a junior doctor opened my door and said with a distinct lack of any enthusiasm or urgency, 'It may be a real fire, come with me.' He seemed to lose interest after that as I was left to my own devices as to where to go. I found a few other unconvinced patients waiting in a lobby area where the ward sister has her desk. 'No, just a practice', we were told by a smiley nurse about thirty seconds later. I was watching the end of the third episode of a terrific BBC series called *Collateral* at the time. Managed to see all four episodes by lunchtime. Was finally released early evening but unhappy to say that they sent me home with that uncomfortable second cannula still stuck in my right arm.

March 2018

Wednesday 14 *Back 'home'*

Good to be back 'home' at The Churchill this morning. Had masses of blood taken, dressings changed, PICC line cleaned, cannula removed, and had a long talk about all side effects with Mus. Saw Emma, Ellie and Monica – all my favourite Churchill people. In fact they were furious about the cannula. It shouldn't have been left attached – the infection risk was very high indeed and a serious complaint was going to be made.

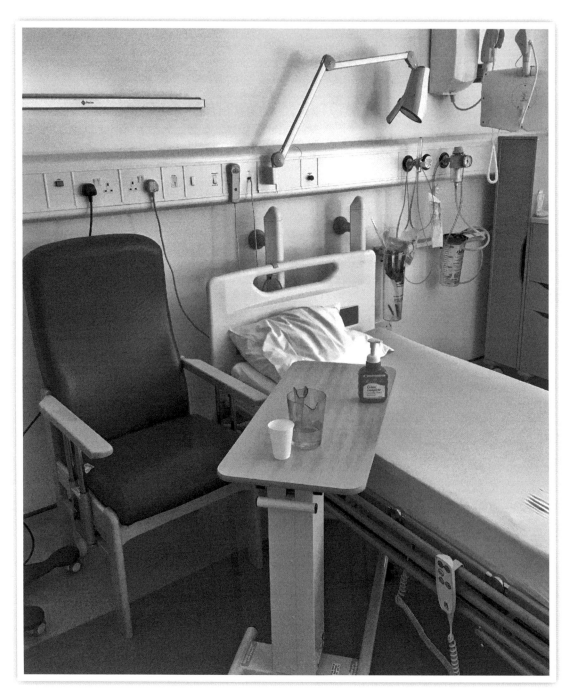

March 2018
Thursday 15   An annoying pill

I've been given an extra antibiotic to take this cycle. It can't be taken within two hours either side of eating or drinking any dairy product. This is proving to be another unexpected complication in my life.

March 2018
Friday 16   More management

It seems to me that cancer treatment is virtually all about managing the side effects. The most important for me at the moment still being the management of constipation, mostly caused by the 'O' chemical in the R-CHOP cocktail – Oncovin. Now, with the latest combination of pills and potions, I've slipped towards the other end of the continuum and now have diarrhoea – which, though strange to say, is hugely preferable. But it needs managing as so much body fluid is lost. So I'll try one fewer dose of Lactulose today as well as drinking virtually non-stop to replace fluids, and see what happens.

March 2018
Saturday 17   Warts and all

Woke up this morning with a small, blood-filled, wart-like growth just under my right eye. A gift from my struggling immune system, no doubt! Rang the hospital and they said there was no need to come in, but just to monitor it carefully. You never know what's coming around the corner. And while I'm moaning, another side effect is sore hands. I would estimate I'm washing my hands about twenty to thirty times a day. I think one begins to get paranoid about everything one touches – better safe than sorry. I'm getting through large quantities of antiseptic hand gel too (which contains a very strong drying agent). And yet another continuing side effect is that bad taste. It seems to be both persistent and shifting in flavour, which annoyingly affects (negatively) the taste of all food and drink. Everything tastes horrible. Eating has become a chore. Has to be done of course, but nothing is good to eat. Nothing, that is, except for some ice cream flavours which do seem palatable. I don't have such a sweet tooth normally, but ice cream does go down well. Thank goodness for that.

March 2018
Tuesday 20   Hair today ... hair tomorrow?

Of course, one infamous and depressing side effect is hair fall-out. Jean told me that if you don't wash your hair – a technique favoured by many – it's less likely to fall out and it self-washes through the production of natural oils (many approve of this and apparently it's good for you). I've found this to be the case.

But you do lose hair in other places. Nasal hair for example. And suddenly you realise why we have it. Without it one is constantly having to blow one's nose. And lack of hair in another place (a little further south) causes much discomfort and necessitates the continual use of powder.

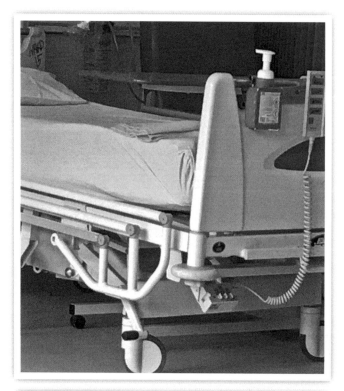

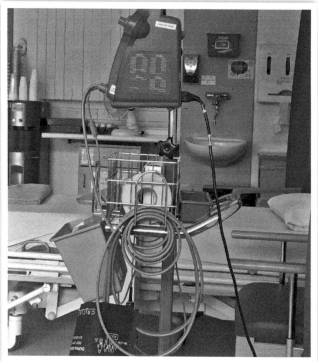

March 2018
Wednesday 21 *Chemo 3*

The past few days, which represent the end of the third week, second cycle, thankfully have been fairly uneventful. I'm now back at The Churchill for the third chemotherapy session. It's quite a milestone as this denotes the half way point. Pleased to find that my weight is just over ten stone. Have put on about two pounds since last official weighing. It's curious how difficult it is to put on weight when you really want to! Especially when trying to avoid a diet of chocolate, biscuits and cakes – I've lost the taste for these foods and they're not nutritionally helpful.

4.55pm

Still here and they've pumped a good few bucketfuls of chemicals into me. The final few mls are being drip-fed as I type. Was taking a bit more notice this time. Cyclophosphamide (or mustard gas) comes in two jumbo-sized syringes which Dot was in charge of today. It looks opaque and each syringe takes quite a while to squeeze in. The Doxorubicin (Hydroxydaunomycin or the H of R-CHOP) is red and causes urine to turn a sort of light rosé colour – but this disappears quickly. The other drugs are slowly drip-fed.

Drinking a lot of water during the process. Think this is a good idea. Means popping into the small room from time to time – and being permanently connected to the drip apparatus (which is on wheels) whilst doing so, makes the procedure quite a challenge (but fun too!).

The last few mls seem to find it difficult to make their journey from the bag, through a small electric pump to the PICC line, and then into the body. They continually set off an alarm caused by air bubbles, which a nurse has to come and switch off and then get the fluid flowing again by flicking the tube with a finger. Eventually finished about six – another long day, but I'm getting better at dealing with it.

March 2018
Thursday 22   *A rather unusual log book*

Following my two really bad experiences with constipation, I really couldn't deal with another one. Have some very good pills and potions now but regulation is imperative. To assist, I've started a log of bowel movements and chosen a rather nice notebook to use, with a picture of the composer Malcolm Arnold on the cover. I've a feeling – with Malcolm's highly mischievous sense of humour – that he would approve. So, at the moment it's Lactulose (a quite nice-tasting honey-like syrup that makes stools softer) twice a day, Laxido (a powder dissolved in liquid that holds water in the stool) once a day and a Senna tablet (which makes you go) in the evenings. Otherwise, day two of cycle three is going well.

Have had good energy and written three piano pieces for the fourth book in my *A Piece a Week* series - a book of short piano pieces aimed at encouraging pianists to actually read music by learning a new, short piece every week. It's exasperating knowing that some aspiring musicians learn maybe only three pieces *a year*! Also watched an excellent BBC programme on Andrew Lloyd Webber which I have to admit has quite changed my impression of him (for the better!).

March 2018
Friday 23   *Depression and friendship*

Evening

Though I had a good day today - good energy levels, a lesson in the morning and a long visit from Jonathan - I became very depressed in the evening. It hadn't really happened before. But bad thoughts flowed into my mind ... of the overpowering boredom (I still have another two and a half months of virtual incarceration, of being cut off from the people and the life I love), and yes, of death. Plus a sudden overwhelming moment when all the side effects, and the side effects of the side effects, seemed to gang up with all their might to taunt me. And this continual bad taste, which makes enjoying food such a trial, was being a particular exasperation. All this was pulling me down into a very unhappy place.

Happily, the amazing Karen Marshall, who obviously has a very well-honed sixth sense, called me at the depth of this depressed state. We talked it all through. We found a lighter side; we talked positively; we laughed. I felt better. Karen advised me to plan ahead and I rang Tony and proposed a ride into Milton Keynes tomorrow for a spot of retail therapy. He agreed and also suggested I took one of the sleeping tablets Dr Noden had prescribed. That was a touch of genius. I take these very rarely (to avoid becoming addicted, or indeed, as Dr Noden put it – for recreational purposes!) but this was the perfect occasion to take one. My sleep is usually very interrupted but a really good night might have a positive effect. I took one and it did. Special friends are playing an extraordinary role in this experience. And I'm blessed to have some very special friends.

March 2018
Saturday 24   *Juice*

As planned, Tony took me to Milton Keynes shopping centre and I bought a juicer. Enjoyed the outing and am especially looking forward to juicing some carrots!

March 2018
Tuesday 27   *Weakness and potential frustration*

I've had a few more 'good-energy' days, but sometimes a day comes along when energy levels are very low and these are difficult to negotiate. It's the chemo drugs really kicking in, a week after the last treatment. Difficult to describe the feeling. It's like trying to operate on a completely empty fuel tank. Focus and concentration don't really happen – major frustration. But best to go with it, accept the situation and show self-compassion. It's the most practical way to deal with it. Fighting it only seems to make it worse. Interestingly, people often talk of 'fighting' cancer. I'm not sure that's the best approach for me. I think my intention is more to defeat it, not fight it. I prefer to think of cancer as a journey, not a battle.

Richard King came to visit in the afternoon which cheered me up hugely. We talked about the publishing world and made some plans, which took my mind to a much more positive place.

March 2018
Wednesday 28   More low energy

What exactly to do on these many low-energy days? Friends say things like, 'you have all this time to read books or watch films.' But in fact I have no inclination to do such things. Without concentration, reading a book is pointless. In fact, just physically picking a book up in this state is near impossible.

March 2018
Friday 30   A very unexpected turn of events

Today marks the start of the National Children's Chamber Orchestra (NCCO) course at Queenswood School in Hatfield. It's one of my favourite weeks of the year. I've been coaching the wind section for quite a few years now and love the enormous enthusiasm and engagement of the wonderful young musicians who take part. I couldn't really see how I was going to manage it this year, what with low energy and immunity levels. But life has an occasional habit of taking you absolutely by surprise.

Yesterday I went to The Churchill for some extra blood tests and was delighted when Emma phoned later in the day to say that my blood actually looked good. She said I could go on the course. Given the fact that my energy levels earlier this week were non-existent, they now seemed to suddenly spring back to life. My very kind and lovely neighbours, Coorous and Mojdeh drove me over to the school and I managed three hours of coaching – on Mozart's wonderful little Overture *Così Fan Tutte* and Tchaikovsky's *Mozartiana* Suite (a really big work). Hugely enjoyed it. Apart from my private teaching, which I've kept up as and when I can, this is the first time I've done any sustained work for quite a long while. Coorous and Mojdeh, who had spent a rainy afternoon in St Albans, then drove me back home for my evening stomach injection.

March 2018
Saturday 31   More NCCO and a fascinating lunch

My energy levels are still up so the very kind Mojdeh drove me to Hatfield again, and this time I took an overnight bag. I'm hoping to stay for a few days. Managed four-and-a-half hours of coaching today, including two chamber music sessions as a result of splitting the ten players of the wind section into two wind quintets. One group did the Malcolm Arnold *Three Shanties* and the other, the Farkas *Old Hungarian Dances*. Still had to be very careful about mixing with potential infection, so, apart from working with my group, kept myself away from other people, on the whole. This meant sitting on my own in a separate room for meals. But a few students came to sit with me at lunchtime, including my pupil Jemma who is now at The Guildhall School of Music and Drama. We talked about the qualities of the 'virtuoso student'. Maybe a future book here?

My number-one quality for a really successful learner of any age is, maybe surprisingly, a sense of personal vulnerability. By this, I mean an absence of arrogance and ego and an acceptance of the true self, an acceptance of where we really are in our learning. Which means not to be fearful of what we can't do or don't know. We sometimes worry that we are going to be 'found out'. Found out for what we don't know, or understand. And this disturbs some people. Some teachers feel this and it stops them from continuing to be good learners themselves. It really doesn't matter. We simply need to accept the situation. This also requires some confidence and courage.

I've also noticed that some teachers occasionally get cross if their pupils can't do things or don't know things – this, if you think logically, is ridiculous. We need to teach pupils to embrace their learning with an open mind and an open heart – never to resist it for any reason. We need to teach them to find their best selves and their true selves. Then we can all truly move forward.

A splendid lunchtime conversation!

April 2018
Tuesday 3 Good and bad news

Still here at NCCO. I can't believe it! Including last Friday have had five days firing on most cylinders. I've done up to six hours coaching a day and feeling very much better for it, psychologically and physically. The energy these terrific young musicians project is really infectious. The bad news today is that the fissure has opened again. Maybe I haven't been drinking enough. I've certainly been trying to regulate the constipation potions as well as I can. But one heavy movement was the troublemaker.

April 2018
Wednesday 4 A very helpful phone call

Back home and Dr Noden rang me this afternoon for his weekly reassuring check-up. I told him about the fissure, which is very painful, and he's prescribed a cream which he says will help matters considerably. This is good news.

April 2018
Saturday 7   *Body repairs*

Been applying the cream (Xyloproct ointment) to the fissure which is still very painful but there are signs of improvement. Constipation regime is now two Senna tablets a day, Laxido in the morning and Lactulose in the afternoon and evening. It's certainly a real challenge to regulate, but essential. Also trying to repair my hands. I've bought some cotton gloves and now go to bed wearing them, along with the application of a generous quantity of extremely good cream. Just give me a top hat and I'd look like a cross between Fred Astaire and a magician.

April 2018
Wednesday 11   *Heart and chemo 4*

9.00am

Turns out that one of the chemo drugs (the H in R-CHOP, Hydroxydaunomycin) can have a deleterious effect on the heart. So, began today with a visit to the sprawling, labyrinthine John Radcliffe Hospital (conveniently just a few minutes from The Churchill) for an echocardiogram. The procedure, which is painless and quite interesting, was carried out by the excellent Linda Arnold.

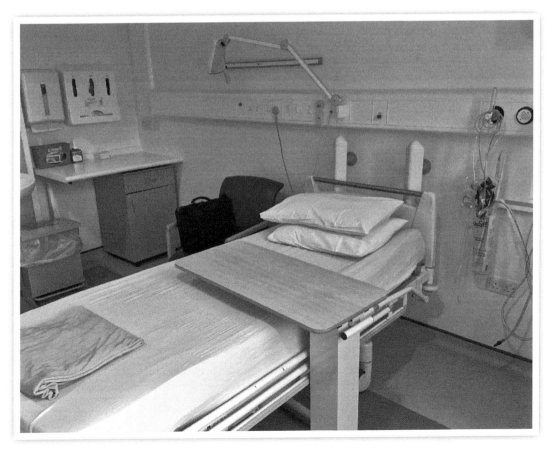

We explored the possibility that she might be related to the Malcolm Arnold family but disappointingly couldn't find any point of connection. The echo test is basically the taking of many pictures of the heart through ultrasound and a little listening to the heart in operation. Some cold jelly is applied to the skin and then Linda held a probe in various positions in order to take 'pictures'. In all it took about forty minutes. Will find out later whether there is any damage. Yet another possible (and potentially serious) side effect. But luckily I am too busy to let this worry me for the time being.

Onward to The Churchill where I was immediately reunited with my three favourite nurses, Ellie, Monica and Hayley. Ellie took an armful of blood. Mus came for a chat and had a look at my fissure, which I'm paranoid about. Evidently it's beginning to heal and he agreed with my constipation dosage. He seemed generally pleased with my progress. I'm hoping that the strength that has materialized through the third cycle will continue into the fourth.

I've put on some weight which I'm very pleased about. Must be all the packets of crisps (salt and vinegar) and ice cream (any flavour – I've become addicted!) I've been eating. Curious how cravings have developed for certain foods I'd never usually eat.

Later saw Emma, my guardian angel, who told me she will be leaving the unit in May. Was very sad to hear this. But Caroline (equally angelic) is taking over as my number-one contact. Emma is moving to London to start a new life in vitamins and Botox injections. I shall miss her.

12.30pm

It seems the heart is not damaged. And my blood is in good condition – so chemo can begin. Phew! It took a little less time than usual and was over in about four hours today. I'm always amused when they inject the cyclophosphamide (mustard gas) through that giant syringe. A volte face of strange and profound significance. So much in life is dependent on context.

April 2018
Thursday 12 *Writing, proof-reading and visitors*

Felt well and strong today, so was able to get on with some proof-reading (Flute *Improve Your Scales* Grade 4–5) and wrote three more pieces for *A Piece a Week*, Book 4. Also taught a lesson and had a couple of visitors. Pleased with today.

April 2018
Saturday 14 *Sleep, sun and Christmas*

The sun came out for about the first time this year and I was able to get out and walk around the garden. Didn't sleep so well last night. Sleep patterns have been very interrupted throughout the whole experience and I'm trying hard to repair them. But feeling a little tired today. Strength still reasonable and wrote the final pieces for *A Piece a Week*, so that manuscript is now complete. Lots of editing and revising to do, always a fun part of the process. Also getting on with a new book, *Clarinet Basics Christmas* – a collection of seasonal pieces and study material for the elementary clarinet player. For the next few weeks I'm going to be humming a lot of Christmas tunes!

April 2018
Sunday 15   *A difficult phone call but consequentially positive thoughts*

Sometimes people say insensitive things that can gravely undermine one's stability. In any verbal transaction we must choose our words carefully – very carefully in fact. To be told, during a phone call with a friend, that there are more serious cancers is actually no help at all. My cancer, to me, is as serious as it gets – whether there are more serious cancers or not. Survival is not assured – though I am extremely positive I will survive. But I need my thoughts, *my* cancer, to be unquestionably validated. I need to be listened to and for others to accept that this is the most serious life experience I've ever had to contend with. There may be a time and place to make comparisons. For example, I was extremely relieved when that initial possibility of pancreatic cancer was dismissed. But, in general, comparisons are not helpful.

Of course I've been doing a lot of thinking, and after these first three months of treatment, have been trying to identify what the experience has already taught me about myself. I've learnt to accept my condition unconditionally and without self-denial, and I've learnt deeper forms of resilience to cope with the multifarious psychological and physical problems that have come my way. How *does* one deal with the unexpected? And there is so much that is unexpected when it comes to cancer. Simply getting it in the first place, and then the endless unexpected side effects. Even when some of them are expected, they can still take you by surprise. In general, by remaining calm and positive, by trying to see problems objectively. And, naturally, I'm continually thinking about the connections with teaching.

*Consequentially, and partly as a result of this phone call, it's become very clear to me that as teachers, we must never dismiss any problem or concern a pupil may have as being unimportant, or less important than a problem another pupil may have. Pupil problems and concerns inevitably have a different perspective in **our** minds. Remember to get into the minds of those pupils and see it from **their** perspective. Each pupil must be listened to and heard meticulously and their concerns treated with the utmost respect and care. To them, at that moment, that problem is probably taking up a good deal of their brain space and requires all our skill, intuition and expertise to deal with it. Never make light of it or suggest it's not that serious. It is serious. Just like my cancer.*

April 2018
Tuesday 17 K.B.O.

The Tuesday after a chemo session has traditionally been a particularly bad day and today is no exception. Virtually no energy, physical or mental. Quite a trial. Really hard to do anything, which is so alien to my natural state. Sometimes can't even think of the correct words, which is really quite scary. My garden has a small central bed and it took me ages to retrieve the word 'lavender', with which it's full. Absolutely no point in fighting it; you just have to go with the flow and let nature take its course. The chemo drugs also affect the blood count, so both red and white levels are down, hence the unpleasant stomach injection every evening. And the drugs attack the whole system, which causes the extreme lethargy. The constant visits to the smallest room are continuing, but taste is not too compromised this cycle, which is good news. Still enjoying my crisps and ice cream! In the words of Sir Winston Churchill, it's a case of 'K.B.O.' – 'keep buggering on'.

April 2018
Wednesday 18 More tests

Tony picked me up at 6.30am for another hospital visit. For the first time it wasn't freezing cold, windy and dark. In fact, for the first time it felt like spring might finally be in the air. Arrived at The Churchill about 7.30am and over coffee, chatted about the new edition of the Malcolm Arnold biography on which we're presently working (Tony rather more than me, at the moment). I'm still feeling weak but can sense some energy returning, thankfully. Just before 8am, made my way upstairs to the EPCTU where Hayley took lots of blood, weighed me (up to 10.10 so still going in the right direction) and changed my PICC line dressing. It's a wait now to see Mus. Hoping to be allowed home mid-morning.

April 2018
Thursday 19 Appetite, injections, warmth, friends and insights

My strength and appetite are still at quite a low level. Today's stomach injection was rather painful. But much happened to make up for all that.

It's the warmest day of the year (the warmest April day since 1949, apparently) and I had a visit from my school friend John, from Bristol. I've written before about friends and how exceptionally important they have been to me in this whole experience. By opening up fully to friends it allows them to react with authenticity and a deep sense of caring. I have found that so many friends want to help and if you accept the situation fully, then they can too. And what a tremendous boon that is. We chatted energetically for much of the day and one particular conversation caused me to think along some fascinating avenues. John is also a teacher (of physics as it happens, though he's also a very accomplished pianist) and this was the basis of that conversation:

Who are you talking to when you teach? Are you talking to yourself? Many teachers are! Are you talking to the instrument ... or to the music on the music stand perhaps ... or just talking into thin air? Or are you talking directly **to** *the pupil? I've seen teachers do each of these. There's enough for a whole chapter here!*

April 2018
Monday 23 A special encounter

I was invited to The Churchill this morning, not for a medical procedure, but to meet a couple of local MPs who are visiting the EPCTU. They were Victoria Prentis (MP for North Oxfordshire) and Robert Courts (who replaced former prime minister David Cameron in the local Witney constituency), accompanied by the head of the unit, Sarah Blagden. I was able to tell them, from a patient's point of view, about the wonderful treatment and staff, and the importance

of the medical research here. The unit is developing and trialling new drugs and treatments as well as deepening the idea that each cancer is on a broad spectrum and, when specifically identified, can be targeted much more accurately. The unit, I told them, was very worthy of all the support they could give it, in whatever fashion. But then the conversation took a surprising turn.

I think I was introduced as 'Mr Harris' (I always think of my father when I hear 'Mr Harris', I never identify with the label!) and after the more important part of our conversation had run its course, Victoria asked me what I do. 'I'm a musician,' I replied, and then when she asked me what instrument I played, a penny seemed to drop with surprising vigour. 'Are you the Paul Harris who writes all the books?' she asked excitedly, to which I answered that, depending on the books, it was a possibility. 'You're a legend in our house!' she exclaimed, with considerable enthusiasm and volume. Her daughter is a clarinettist and then a whole extraordinary stream of coincidences tumbled out. Her teacher is a great friend. I've actually given the young Miss Prentis a lesson at a workshop in Oxford and Victoria lives virtually next door to another very good friend of mine! This second half of our conversation became very animated indeed and poor old Robert was left rather on the periphery. It was both a fun and an important encounter and I was delighted to have been invited to the hospital to have it.

April 2018
Tuesday 24   A sleepy visit

A low energy day but a visit from my great friend Robert Tucker in the evening cheered me up. Rob is head of music at the local Royal Latin School and often pops in. Not sure I managed to stay awake for the duration of his visit but knowing it didn't matter is very comforting.

April 2018
Wednesday 25 *An annoyance*

Despite my best and exhaustive efforts to keep constipation under control, the fissure has opened up yet again today. I'm taking medicines five times a day at the moment, which means I'm spending a disproportionate amount of my life thinking about the problem – and still I can't quite get it right. I spoke to Dr Noden who suggested an extra dose of Laxido just for the time being. That'll be constipation medicines *six times a day*. I'll try that and hope for the best. It's extremely painful when it happens and I'd really rather it didn't.

April 2018
Thursday 26 *Games*

My friends Paul and Spider Hayler visited today. Paul taught me A level geology at school and I hugely enjoyed the subject (it seemed to fit in very well alongside music and history!). The Haylers are deeply kind and warm-hearted and we spent the afternoon playing board games and laughing. The perfect antidote.

May 2018
Tuesday 1 *May Day, appraisals and third week*

May Day! I managed to get up to Stowe School music department this morning where I've been asked to observe and appraise lessons given by the visiting music staff. (Emma said I can get out and about a bit more now as my blood count seems to be a little more normal and an extra antibiotic I'm taking to help prevent infection seems to be doing its job.) It's always a privilege

and certainly fascinating to sit in on lessons – I'm constantly intrigued by the process of teaching and seeing how others do it is always a treat. I was reminded that when I used to teach at Stowe, we celebrated May Day morning with a short outdoor concert given at the crack of dawn by my clarinet quartet, followed by a very generous breakfast cooked on large camping gas stoves.

I have come to expect the third week of the chemo cycle as usually the calmest and least challenging. Have generally had good strength and appetite, and been managing most of the side effects fairly resourcefully. My hands are still a problem though. They seem to have gone a curious darker colour, especially the nail bed above the cuticle, and are still very dry and rather tight. Strangely, each nail reflects each chemo session by the development of a ridge. This, evidently, is the Cyclophosphamide at work. Extraordinary what chemotherapy does to the body. And goodness knows what else it's doing that one has no conception of. I now have a collection of four different hand creams to help my hands. Also I've discovered that most soaps (both liquids and bars) contain a nasty ingredient called sodium laureth sulfate (SLES), a known irritant. Have found an amazing soap that is free from nasties and now use it in place of all others.

May 2018
Wednesday 2   Chemo 5

Arrived at The Churchill just after 7.30am, thanks to Tony's continued kindness. It was yet another cold, wet and windy start, so his new car, with its particularly effective heating system, was much appreciated. Spring seems very reluctant to make an appearance. Lots of good chatter in the car. Tony was a housemaster at Stowe School for many years and he gave me a potted history of his predecessors. We also spoke of Philip Browne – first Director of Music at Stowe and composer of (among many other works) *A Truro Maggot* – a lovely little occasional piece for clarinet and piano. After our customary coffee I made my way up to the EPTCU and was met immediately by Ellie, whose last day at The Churchill it is today.

Had lots of blood taken and then an ECG to check the heart again. Ten sticky pads were attached to various parts of my body and then an electrode connected to each. The process was over in a moment but then the laborious removal of the sticky pads began. It's a tough job because of the amount of body hair I have. For some reason none of that has fallen out! To minimize pain (of which I evidently have quite a low threshold), each pad has to be painstakingly detached with the aid of special alcohol-soaked tissues. (All was made a little more fun by a rather racy conversation with nurse Eliana on the subject of waxing!) 'Obs' done (all good) and then a visit to the scales – disappointingly, my weight hasn't increased much since last time, despite still consuming considerable quantities of salt and vinegar crisps and ice cream!

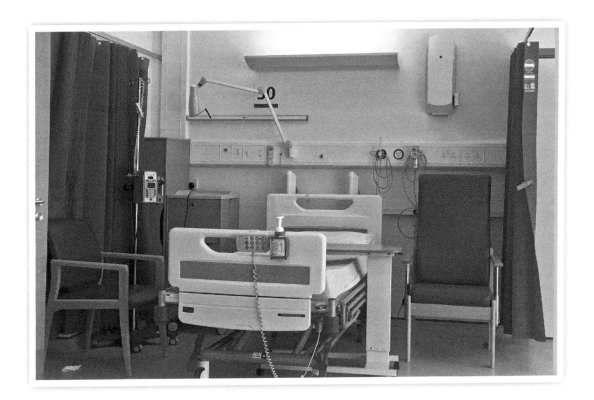

I saw Mus and we had a brief conversation on how all is going and then Emma, my guardian angel, popped in to see me prior to delivering all the chemo drugs. This will be the last time I see Emma here as she's leaving before my next visit. Chemo start time delayed till 1pm as the company who produce the drugs are behind schedule today. Slightly annoying, given that I've been here since 7.30am. Finally completed the process just before 6.00pm. A long day, but I'm coping fairly well with chemo days now.

May 2018
Thursday 3   Hiccups

Today a new side effect emerged – hiccups, caused yet again by the chemotherapy. They began mid-evening and continued for nearly three hours. It's a very unpleasant experience so I phoned the hospital and the duty consultant suggested I increased my dosage of Metaclopromide, an anti-sickness drug that I take every day. It seemed to do the trick, thankfully. You really never do know what's coming around the corner.

May 2018
Tuesday 8   Brain shut-down and empathising with lethargy

It's extreme weakness time again. And I'm trying to find a way of describing it. I think 'brain shut-down' expresses the situation fairly well! There's a disinclination to do anything; physical and mental energy are at zero. Focus and concentration are very low, it's a struggle even to move. In this state I can empathize with those who have no motivation to do anything. And that's quite interesting.

*As teachers, we all have a range of strategies for attempting to motivate our less driven pupils to put in greater effort. We might use words (inspirational or otherwise), imaginative illustrations, modelling, or maybe rewards. But in **my** present state none of these would make any difference. This is an extreme form of de-motivation. It's curiously useful to experience it, in a way.*

But, for someone who is usually dashing about thinking and doing, it remains a very frustrating place to be. It's the cocktail of toxic chemo drugs doing their job that is causing this reaction, so one has to go with it and simply wait for the lethargy to wear off. Even though I'm used to it now it's still not easy to manage.

The bad taste, dry hands and other side effects still persist. I have also been noticing numbness in my toes (especially the left set) and a little in the fingers. This has been the case for some time, though Mus is not too concerned. It's not quite severe enough to put on their scale of numbness, but can be treated if it becomes more of a problem. I am a little worried as the fingers, of course, are extremely important to me and I have heard that this can develop into a major problem for some. It's called Peripheral Neuropathy and is caused by the Vincristine (curiously the 'O') of the R-CHOP cocktail. Controlling constipation remains a full-time job. But there we are. K.B.O. ...

May 2018
Wednesday 9 *Scan date*

I received a letter with the date of my very important post-treatment scan today. The scan that will reveal whether the tumour, and thus the cancer, has been defeated. Although I have another chemotherapy cycle to go through, I somehow feel confident that the cancer has been cured and the tumour is gone. But it's impossible not to experience a certain niggling doubt and however hard one tries to dismiss it, that uncertainty won't go away. That sixty to seventy percent survival rate is very hard to dismiss.

May 2018
Friday 11 *Christmas again*

Lesley, my wonderful editor and friend from Faber Music, came over today to help adapt my completed *Christmas Clarinet Basics* into a flute version. Energy levels were good and it was great to be fully engaged in some highly enjoyable and stimulating work. We completed virtually the whole flute part in one day. It contains arrangements of about forty Christmas tunes – that's virtually all there are! Plus various seasonal studies and exercises I've written especially for the volume. Still quite a bit of work to do on the piano accompaniments, but invigorating and satisfying to make such progress on another book.

May 2018
Tuesday 15   *Bassoon Basics*

More writing today. My wonderful bassoonist friend Emily arrived early morning to begin work with me on a major new bassoon tutor. We're going to use my clarinet tutor, *Clarinet Basics*, as the structure. It will need a lot of fresh material and so will provide lots of scope for composing new music. Very pleased to be setting off on another exciting publishing adventure!

May 2018
Wednesday 23   *Chemo 6*

Arrived at the EPCTU for my last hospital chemo – number six. Missing Emma but was greeted by the cheery Monica and Hayley. I've come to feel a real affection for this place and the lovely staff here. There is a kindness and warmth in the atmosphere. I was sent to bed 33 today, which is in a small bay with two other beds. Maddie, a very personable student nurse from Oxford Brookes University, dealt with my 'obs' and ECG (followed by the usual fun removing the sticky pads) and we talked about the importance of empathy.

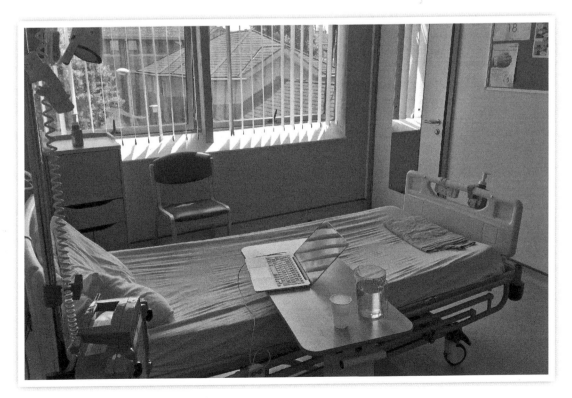

She had recently been set an essay on the subject and evidently there had been some discussion on the pros and cons. Maddie came out in favour I'm glad to say. For medics and teachers, empathy *has* to be one of their primary qualities.

I had a good chat to Mus about the next stage. After this three-week cycle there will be two further cycles of a month each, but just taking the much less aggressive pill Acalabrutinib (known as an inhibitor) twice a day at home. Being rid of the R-CHOP chemicals should begin to make a big difference. Especially looking forward to getting my taste back.[7]

7 https://en.wikipedia.org/wiki/Acalabrutinib

Chemo went okay; just took four and a half hours today. Also had my PICC line taken out which proved rather more painful than expected, requiring pulling out a staple, now embedded well under the skin – really not a pleasant experience. However, looking forward to life without that bulky contraption permanently connected to my left arm.

May 2018
Saturday 26 Fed up

Just occasionally I feel fed up, and today is such a day. Ninety-nine percent of the time I remain entirely positive but sometimes things do catch up. The lack of energy and ability to concentrate, the endless pill-taking, the constant monitoring of constipation, the various bodily functions that don't quite work, the nasty taste … all these do, very occasionally, cause depression. And it takes quite an effort to ignore it. Somehow one needs to find sufficient energy in order to deal with the lack of energy – a strangely paradoxical situation!

May 2018
Sunday 27 China

I should have been setting off for China today, for a week presenting talks on Simultaneous Learning (a form of teaching I've devised) in eight different cities around the country. Very disappointing to be stuck here! But delighted that Bill Thomson will be representing me instead. Many of my books are now being published in Chinese editions. Having visited last year I was thrilled that so many teachers seemed to be excited by what I had to say. The kind of inclusive and less authoritarian teaching I advocate seemed to go down well with the many teachers I spoke to. I know Bill is going to have a great time. I'm hoping to go back to China next year to carry on the good work.

May 2018
Monday 28   Injection

Jenny came to give me my stomach injection this evening – it was definitely the best one ever, hardly felt it at all!

May 2018
Thursday 31   A counter-intuitive thought and a bit of crystal-ball gazing

Richard Crozier came round for lunch today. Richard is a very eminent music educator; together we wrote *The Music Teacher's Companion*[8]. I ate very little as my appetite has gone again. Appetite is so up and down: for the first four days after the last chemo I could hardly stop eating as the steroid Prednisolone was added to my daily diet of pills. Steroids really boost the appetite. Now it's gone the other way and I'm struggling to eat anything. It's been a difficult post-chemo session this time in every way. But we indulged in much excellent conversation and Richard made a most interesting point. When we're ill we

8 *The Music Teacher's Companion: A Practical Guide*, Richard Crozier and Paul Harris (ABRSM Publishing, 2000)

Me and my daily diet of pills

usually go to the doctor and get a pill that makes us better. When it comes to cancer, we get many (many) pills and potions, and for six months or so they make us feel (much) worse. Somehow one has to get used to this counter-intuitive process. But it's all in an excellent cause of course. We speculated what cancer treatment might be like in a few years' time. Also what medicine might be like in the future. Hopefully these interminable months of gruelling treatment might be reduced to something far briefer and less punishing.

June 2018
Friday 1   A troubling pain

I have an intermittent pain in an area very close to the tumour (somewhere just above the stomach) – can't help but worry about this. The Macmillan Cancer Support website says that this is not uncommon, but I will monitor it carefully.

June 2018
Monday 4   More pain

Rang the hospital about the persistent pain and spoke to Caroline, who told me not to worry unless it gets worse. Easier said than done, but I'll try.

June 2018
Tuesday 5   A bassoon day

Emily and I finished working on *Bassoon Basics* today. Very pleased with the result and very exciting to add a bassoon tutor to the family! There's going to be a Chinese edition soon too. In the evening, by an amazing coincidence, I had a visit from another bassoon player, Will, who lives locally and is a student at the Royal Academy of Music. I managed to find enough energy to play the Beethoven Duos for clarinet and bassoon with him. Most enjoyable.

June 2018
Thursday 7   Messages from China

I heard from Bill Thomson today that all goes well on his Chinese adventure. It's very humbling to know that Bill is there talking about Simultaneous Learning and my books in general.

June 2018
Tuesday 12   A Piece a Week

I received the first full set of proofs for *A Piece a Week* Book 4 and did my proof-reading this morning. Played through all twenty-seven pieces and found very little on which to comment. Pleased with this series and now have to put my mind to Book 5. Feels quite a mountain to climb. Writing short succinct character pieces is not easy.

June 2018
Wednesday 13   *No chemo*

This would normally be a chemo day as it represents the end of the sixth cycle. But I've had my six doses now. Feels odd not to be taking the crack-of-dawn trip over to Oxford. But not having a load more chemicals pumped into me today does mean that all those side effects should begin to recede. How long this will take is one of the first questions I shall ask Mus on Friday when I go for my next appointment. I understand that hair begins to regrow soon after chemo stops, so I'm monitoring the hair on my arms, eyebrows and eyelashes (all of which have disappeared), maybe rather too punctiliously! It seems that a watched hair never grows.

June 2018
Thursday 14   *Uncertainties*

Felt quite troubled today. Even though I feel confident that this is all going to work out well, there's that small chance that it might not. And it's not possible to exorcize these thoughts. I don't really have any idea what the alternative is – not too good, I think. We only get one go at treating this cancer, which I've known from the start[9]. But important to process these thoughts rather than ignore them, which I'm sure creates an unhealthy background tension and stress. Feeling a bit sick which I'm guessing is more psychological than physical. Rather indulgently watching loads of episodes of *The Crown* on Netflix (which I'm much enjoying) and Tony is taking me to another antiques emporium near Northampton this afternoon. Keeping my practice up, too, for a recital at the Buckingham Festival in July. It will be my first public appearance since early February. Keeping busy and distracted certainly helps control the worrying thoughts.

9 Since I wrote this I believe that further treatments are now possible.

Had my usual call from Dr Noden this afternoon – possibly the last as he's moving on from the Buckingham practice to a new life in Devon. I had wanted to take him out for a meal to say thank you for all the support he has given me, as well as for taking me seriously from my very first appointment – he could so easily have sent me home with a 'let's see if the discomfort has gone in a couple of weeks'. This may have been a life-saving decision. But it turns out that he's not allowed to accept my invitation. What strange rules we have these days.

The big day

Up at 6am and it's a lovely day. The sun is shining – it feels almost Mediterranean. So different from those early hospital days back in the winter months. Feeling apprehensive but also eager to get to The Churchill and begin moving towards the conclusion of this life-changing experience. Whatever that may be. Strangely hardly any traffic this morning and arrived at the hospital before 7.30am. Not only were the roads quiet but The Churchill seems to be quiet too. Not the usual hustle and bustle, even at this time of the morning. Tony and I had a coffee and a croissant.

Went up to the EPCTU just after 8am and was greeted by Hayley. She's one of the few nurses left from that wonderful original crew. Was sent to comfortable room 18 where I've been a number of times before. The sun is streaming in through the generous windows. Having now lost my PICC line, Hayley fitted a cannula (also needed for the scan this afternoon) and did her phlebotomy. Then gave me a full service, the usual 'obs', an ECG (had to remove all those pesky pads) and took my weight which has now risen to just under eleven stone. I offered a brief and silent 'thank-you' to all those sinful packets of crisps and ice creams! Now I'm waiting to see Mus and then the scan at 2pm.

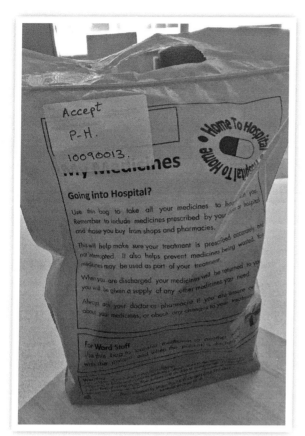

11.30am

Just seen Mus and we talked through the next couple of months. Just have to take the Acalabrutinib tablets every day – a much less aggressive drug than the R-CHOP cocktail. This means that I won't have to continue acting the part of walking dispensary, as many of the vast number of daily pills I've been taking can be cut out. I was worried about the constipation but Mus says this should begin to return to normal soon, so suggested I reduce the various pills and potions, but not stop them. My red blood count was pretty normal and white blood count improving so I'll be able to begin mixing in public again soon. And no more stomach injections. Thank goodness for that! But he did say that it would take between three and six months to begin getting properly back to normal. Not sure if I can remember what that is like.

A little later Dot came to see me with my much-reduced pill load and instructions for cycle 7. Rather depressingly she said that I might not hear the result of today's scan until well into next week. For me this really is the most important piece of news I'll *ever* be waiting for. There doesn't seem to be the same degree of urgency about it here. Not so good for the stress levels.

1.15pm

Arrived at the Radiology Department 45 minutes early as required and surprisingly had the scan almost immediately. It was all very quick and painless (partly due to the cannula, which saved me from a couple more injections). The big doughnut-like machine is a bit intimidating – I kept my eyes closed and hummed some Mozart during the scan, which lasted about twenty minutes. Afterwards, I asked the scanner crew if they might try to release the result as soon as possible, as I really was rather keen to know it. They agreed, though I suspect the matter is probably not within their remit. So now it's just down to waiting ...

June 2018
Sunday 17

The waiting game and a lovely concert

It's been a difficult weekend. Felt very tired yesterday and not that well. Almost certainly a reaction to Friday's psychologically challenging events and having to get up very early. Some inevitable anxiety and stress. Feeling better today, though appetite and taste both poor. Still not much pleasure to be found in food. However, I went to a lovely concert in Oxford this afternoon – the first I've been to for about six months. It was presented by the Incorporated Society of Musicians (ISM). I'm now a committee member for the Oxford branch and this was my first event in that capacity. The concert's theme (my idea) was duets played by teacher and pupil. I thought it would be both inspirational and aspirational. My lovely friend Jean had many excellent pupils playing.

June 2018
Monday 18

An extraordinary day

It didn't begin well. I fainted. I have felt faint many times over the past few months – again a side effect of the drugs, but have managed never actually to do so. It was just after I got up and happened in the bathroom. I found myself on the floor. I don't think I was out for very long. There was quite a gash on my left-hand little finger and a good deal of blood, but I didn't notice the position of that finger until a little later. I think I must have caught it on the radiator.

Jean came round to offer moral support for my phone call to the hospital. Rang about 11am but Mus wasn't available. I left a message. He rang back about an hour later with some words that will forever be fixed in my mind. He told me: 'the tumour has melted away.' To say I was relieved is of course a colossal understatement. Difficult to explain quite what I felt. Six months of trauma, worry, dark thoughts, and the tremendous energy required to stay on top of things takes a massive toll. So the complexity of thoughts is not surprising. I rang and messaged those closest to me to share the news.

After a celebratory walk around nearby Rousham Gardens, we noticed that my left-hand little finger wasn't where it should have been. And the hand had swollen considerably. Jean and I played a clarinet duet and I found I couldn't play the left-hand little-finger keys. My finger was sticking out at an alarming angle in relation to the hand, and I had no control over it. What a sting in the tail and extraordinary bad luck. My Buckingham Festival recital on July 11 (for which I had been doing quite a bit of practice) suddenly looked very unlikely. On a day that should have been blissfully happy, I was left with another worry and felt very depressed.

June 2018
Tuesday 19 *Serious hand trouble*

Rang up my local surgery at opening time and was given an appointment at 9.10am. I was worried about infection to the gash but when I told Dr Caroline (who turns out to be a very enthusiastic violinist) that I was a clarinettist she was instantly worried about the position of the finger – the gash held very little interest to her at all. She thought something might be broken and said she would get me an immediate appointment with the plastic surgery unit at Stoke Mandeville and would ring soon with times. The wound was dressed by the nurse and I went home, not in the best of spirits.

In fact Caroline rang about forty minutes later with instructions to go straight to Milton Keynes A&E. My neighbour Mojdeh very kindly drove me over to Milton Keynes. A&E is not a place I would ever choose to spend my time. And I was supposed to be delivering a talk to the Stowe School Music Department just after lunch. So I sat there in a state of considerable frustration. I should have been feeling something not far short of euphoria, but instead I was exasperated by this piece of really bad misfortune.

I had an X-ray and eventually, some hours later, saw a duty doctor. We looked at the X-ray together and she got me doing some hand and finger movements, concluding that nothing was broken. I told her that being a professional clarinet player this was all rather concerning and of paramount importance to me. I was truly shocked by her astounding response, 'What is a clarinet?' It turned out her medical judgement was pretty wide of the mark too. The wound was dressed again and I was sent home without further comment. I rang for a taxi and we sped over to Stowe. I'd missed my slot and the departmental day was coming to an end, but Hilary Davan Wetton, who was chairing the day, allowed me to give my short presentation on what makes a good head of faculty. This cheered me up – it was the first time I had spoken in public for about seven months.

June, 2018
Monday 25   Complex times

There was no improvement to the hand a week later. My recital at the Buckingham Festival in a couple of weeks' time is not looking too promising as I can't practise or play productively – my little finger remaining stiff and in the wrong place. Frustratingly (very frustratingly, in fact) I can't find the little-finger notes. So, an appointment was made for a visit to the Milton Keynes Hospital Fracture Unit.

Psychologically still very unsettled. In fact, thinking of seeing a counsellor. Feeling troubled by a sense of uncertainty, anxiety and lack of confidence about the future. Suddenly things are different. The daily routine I've been used to these past months, though rarely much fun, has evaporated. Six months of trauma is quite something to contend with but now looking into this new future is strangely and unexpectedly disturbing. The road back to 'normal' life is a lot more complex than you'd think. I wasn't prepared for this reaction.

June 2018
Wednesday 27   Hospital again

Tony picked me up for my 10.45am appointment at Milton Keynes Fracture clinic. More waiting in yet another waiting area … forty-minute delay … eventually I was summoned to a small consulting room where a youngish doctor sat peering at his computer screen. I think my first exchange with him was perhaps a bit provocative, but I really was in no mood for a perfunctory meeting. After I entered he left the door wide open. 'Door open or closed?' I asked. 'Open is fine,' he replied, somewhat disinterestedly. 'I'd rather it closed, it would make me feel we're taking this a bit more seriously,' I responded belligerently. He looked a little surprised but the door was shut. To give the doctor his due, he did a thorough examination of my hand and concluded (incorrectly, as it turned out) that no ligaments, tendons or bones were broken. He told me, though, that the swelling might take two months to repair and the finger might never go back to its proper position. This left me feeling very depressed. But this was not the end of this visit. He then told me to see the hand therapist just down the corridor.

Clare, the therapist, had a jolly demeanour and a reassuringly positive outlook on life. When I entered the hand therapy room she was working with a young lad who had injured his hand in a football accident. I listened to her as she gave him his exercises and reassured him that all will be well. After he left, she came, with her laptop, to sit by me at the table I had chosen. I offered her a potted history of the events that had led me here, which she typed, reluctantly, into her shiny new laptop. 'I hate this new system,' she bemoaned. 'Everything now has to be typed up as we go along.' We both noticed quite a number of spelling mistakes but it didn't seem to bother her. Clare was much more encouraging and upbeat than the doctor. 'They're very pessimistic in the Fracture Unit,' she volunteered, and gave me a battery of hand and finger exercises to do every day. 'It'll most likely get better,' she informed me, which made me feel a little more confident. She also gave me two golf balls which were required for one of the hand exercises.

Tony came to pick me up and I was grateful to be able to unload the very mixed set of messages I had just received. I arrived home feeling fairly unhappy.

June 2018
Thursday 28 *Confusion*

Most people, understandably, would think that receiving the good news about the success of my lymphoma treatment would be immensely cheering. There is a future. The treatment has worked. But the reality is not so clear cut. All these months of uncertainty, thoughts of mortality and the energy required to keep on top of things, have left me feeling mentally exhausted. I'm sure time will heal, but it will take a while. And there is also an attendant confidence issue. I struggle to answer emails and make plans. Six months of isolation have produced a strange kind of cabin fever. It seems I have become institutionalised to the (abnormal) routine of three-weekly chemotherapy cycles, numerous other hospital visits, poor sleeping patterns, constant pill taking, low energy, sundry side effects and an absence of most of the regular exciting events that used to be my daily routine. And, understandably, a number of friends who had been keeping in close contact have stopped doing so. Maybe they are thinking, 'what can we do now?', assuming that the worst is over.

Oddly it isn't.

The transition back into 'normal' life is not easy. My self-belief has been destabilized and energy levels are down. I'm sure these will return, but they feel a little remote at the moment.

July 2018
Wednesday 4   *Therapy and practice*

I have booked to see a therapist. Need some practical help on how to deal with the trauma fallout. I'm finding 'one small step at a time' is helpful at the moment, but always worth consulting an expert. I am practising *a lot* and beginning to get around those little finger notes – the recital is now looking a lot more promising, thanks to sheer determination.

July 2018
Thursday 5   *Identity issues*

I think I can see a little growth in my eyebrows today. That cheered me up! Though I have maintained my no-hair-wash policy (that doesn't apply to the rest of the body, by the way), much hair has nevertheless fallen out and of course this is depressing. One's appearance is certainly part of one's identity and if this changes dramatically it has a profound effect on confidence and inner strength. They say it might or might not grow back. Oh well … I shall just have to wait and see. I'm considering the Bruce Willis look, plus a new pair of thicker framed spectacles. A new appearance for my new lease of life actually begins to appeal.

July 2018
Friday 6   *A new future*

I have been thinking about this 'new lease of life', for that is what it is. There was always that thirty to forty percent chance that my treatment could have been unsuccessful – and I have no idea what that would have actually meant, aside from not much of a future. But, thankfully, I do have a future. Through the wonderful help of many doctors and nurses and friends I have managed to survive, and now feel I am at a place where I need to think carefully about that future. Do I continue exactly as before or make some changes … and are those changes small or large? Just as one's appearance contributes significantly to one's identity, so does one's work. What you do is a major part of who you are. It's certainly an interesting dilemma.

One of my guiding principles has always been to make the best of each and every day. I feel that more strongly than ever now.

July 2018
Sunday 8   *Playing music again*

Had a rehearsal of Mozart's wonderful Kegelstatt Trio, K.498 for next Wednesday's concert with Robert Secret (viola) and Helen Davies (piano). So good to be playing gorgeous chamber music again. Then drove over to

Cambridge to rehearse the rest of the programme with Flora Tzannetaki (two lovely sonatas by early nineteenth-century composer Jean Xavier Lefèvre and various other showy, shorter pieces). Quite the busiest day I've had for a *very* long time. Energy levels very good.

July 2018
Monday 9   Fingers and practice

My finger and hand are still not a whole lot better. But practising is going well for Wednesday's recital and I am continuing to do lots of hand exercises. A friend very thoughtfully brought round a little finger-strengthening device over the weekend, of which I'm making good use.

July 2018
Wednesday 11   Concert-giving

Recital day. I can hardly believe I've got here. Just six weeks ago it looked improbable and then, with the finger injury, even less so. But here we are, at the Radcliffe Centre, which is a lovely small concert hall, part of Buckingham University. It was virtually a sell-out and went well. I presented the concert as if I had invited the audience into my music room at home to share some lovely music. The atmosphere had a warm and intimate quality and it was wonderful to play with such superb musicians and friends. A real confidence booster.

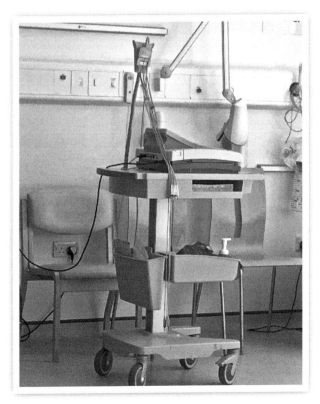

July 2018
Friday 13   An emotional visit

Back at The Churchill for the usual tests and chats. Installed in room 18. Andrea was phlebotomy general today and annoyingly I wasn't giving blood easily. It took about four attempts to find a compliant vein. Had a lovely chat to Hayley and we agreed that I would buy a fridge for the nurses' room. The staff here have been exceptionally caring and kind; it will be a very small token of enormous appreciation and gratitude. Had my usual chat with Mus who gave me my next set of pills and instructions (much reduced). The next visit will be in a month's time, and I'll be returning for check-ups and scans every three months after that for two more years. Interestingly it's not until then that they can tell you whether the cancer has been absolutely beaten.

Felt rather wistful and emotional as I left the EPCTU today. To say that I've enjoyed my many visits here is maybe not quite the right word (though, strangely, maybe it is …), but I've been treated so well over all these months and have come to form a very special relationship with the wonderful doctors and nurses – I will miss them enormously.

July 2018
Saturday 14   Oboe time

Leigh – oboist, friend and my former Faber Music editor – came over today to begin working on *Oboe Basics*, a beginner's tutor for the oboe. Like *Bassoon Basics*, we'll use my clarinet version as a starting point. It will mean re-arranging some existing material, writing new material and finding appropriate pieces to give beginner oboists a good progressive start. Exciting to get going on yet another shiny new project.

July 2018
Friday 20   A hair-raising experience

Took a sleeping tablet this evening as sleep has been even worse than usual recently. Soon started dreaming that I was scratching my head, accompanied by a nightmarish vision of pulling out handfuls of hair. For some surreal moments I thought that it was indeed a nightmare, but very soon realised that it actually was happening! I *was* pulling out handfuls of hair. So, in my slightly dozy state, I had a shower and all my remaining hair came out. I knew what hair I had wasn't really attached at all. So I am now sporting the full Bruce Willis look. It was a very curious experience but I'm being quite philosophical about it.

July 2018
Saturday 21   The psychology of appearance

Have been trying to rationalise the appearance thing. I understand the potential loss of self-esteem that comes with loss of hair. But I'm not going there. I intend to wear my new look with confidence. I'm sure if one presents oneself to others with assurance and poise and without any sense of anxiety or embarrassment, then they can similarly respond without any sense of discomfort, awkwardness or indeed pity.

July 2018
Thursday 26   More hand problems ...

I had an appointment with a plastic surgeon at the John Radcliffe Hospital in Oxford today. My hand has shown no sign of improving – still swollen, with the little finger out of place. Evidently I will need an operation to put it right which will put me out of (clarinet-playing) action for about two months. Major frustration. Having an MRI scan soon.

August 2018
Monday 6   ... but more hair

My hair does seem to be growing back, but I actually like the new look and am thinking of keeping whatever grows back very short. I am noticing, when out, quite how many people are sporting the Bruce Willis look these days. It's clearly highly fashionable.

August 2018
Tuesday 7   Expert chatter

I have now had three sessions with Jeremy, a delightful therapist. It's very good to talk with someone who is independent and brings an expert view and understanding to the kind of problems that six months of trauma can create. Good therapists cause you to see your reality a little more clearly. And whilst there's nothing I'm telling Jeremy that I don't tell close friends, I feel that I am not putting any emotional pressure on him. I can talk to him without any sense that he might be burdened by my problems. Telling someone quite independent, who hardly knows me, *is* therapeutic. It's as though the words and thoughts are being processed and then consumed by someone else. The troubled thoughts begin to fade.

August 2018
Wednesday 8   Matters of the heart

I went to the John Radcliffe Hospital in Oxford today for another echocardiogram, to check whether the chemotherapy cocktail has damaged the heart. It's quite a painless procedure but takes about an hour. I should get the results on Friday. It was expertly carried out by a student doctor, overseen by the excellent Linda who performed the task last time.

August 2018
Thursday 9   *Re-energising*

My energy is beginning to return – difficult to remember quite what running on a full tank is like, but feeling that I'm getting there. My sense of humour is also returning to its old self – not that I ever lost it, but it is enjoying something of a resurgence. I've always believed deeply in a sense of humour. There really is a lighter side to almost everything – and finding that lighter side is a great help in managing most challenges that life throws your way. Having a sense of humour and an absence of a sense of entitlement are two of my most important life principles. It's amazing, with those two beliefs driving you forward, how easily you can deal with most of life's problems.

August 2018
Friday 10   *Final visit to the EPCTU (for the time being)*

Tony picked me up at 6.30am, our usual departure time, but because it's August and school holidays there was virtually no traffic on the roads and we arrived by 7.15am. Had the customary coffee at the café plus an indulgent croissant today. Was installed in Room 16 and Andrea, who took my blood last time, popped in and offered me a jug of water. Kindness when you don't necessarily expect it is doubly special. It's a great quality that sadly too few seem to exhibit.

Dina, a new nurse from Spain, fitted a cannula – a bit painful as the needle was evidently thicker than usual, so as to be appropriate for the later scan, as well as for taking blood now. Had a good chat to Hayley and am now waiting for more tests and to see Mus. Caroline popped in to give me my next appointment which will be another scan and tests in three months' time.

10.45am

Have had the full gamut of tests now. Dina asked if I was a sportsman! Never been asked that before. Evidently my heart rate is that of a sporty person (a good thing!). I explained that being a clarinettist requires a lot of physical effort, especially in the breathing department. We agreed this was a healthy occupation and probably the cause of her assumption.

1.00pm

Another ultrasound scan followed by a chat with Mus. We discussed my lingering side effects, but the major excitement was when he told me, 'You're now a free man.' That means I can drink orange juice again and go on public transport! I thanked him profusely for the extraordinarily wonderful way I've been looked after these past seven months.

It's certainly good to be a free man, but I'm glad that I'll be paying the EPCTU the first of two years' worth of follow-up visits in November.

August 2018
Wednesday 15 *Denmark and work*

Morning

Popped over to Denmark for my first big journey and two days of presentations. My first work of this nature for eight months. I'm speaking in Copenhagen for four and a half hours on Simultaneous Learning and being a Virtuoso Teacher. I'm very excited and eager but also feeling anxious about stamina, energy, memory and whether my voice will stand up to the challenge.

Evening

It turns out that I needn't have worried. All went well. The hundred or so teachers seemed pleased and content. I was pleased and content. And didn't feel at all tired at the end. But afterwards I found myself, curiously, in questioning mode again. I love this work indisputably, but my brain was asking whether it's the right thing to be doing. I know it is. But having been through such a traumatic and life-threatening experience maybe one simply *has* to question everything. The brain demands a re-think. Happily I ended the day with a hint of a solution beginning to emerge.

August 2018
Friday 17 *Results*

Rang Mus this morning to ask him about the results of last week's tests and scan. He said I couldn't be given an absolutely clean bill of health as there was a little shadow or scarring still evident. But it was nothing to worry about. The heart is good, though white blood count still a little low. Exercise is the answer, he told me.

August 2018
Saturday 18 *Some answers*

I'm beginning to make some sense of these perplexing thoughts that have been invading my thinking these past weeks. With the passing of time I'm at last seeing them a little more clearly and strategies are forming.

August 2018
Tuesday 21   *Orange juice*

Bought eight oranges this morning to make fresh orange juice. It's been a struggle living without oranges, grapefruit and their respective juices and derivatives for so long. Went out for a long walk this afternoon to create a few more white blood cells.

August 2018
Wednesday 22   *More anxiety*

Woke up feeling anxious and uncertain again. Trying to bring some cold logic to these feelings but it's not easy. They come and go and seem quite alien to my normal psychological state. Such an unexpected side effect.

August 2018
Friday 24   *A lot of potential hand exercises*

Made a return visit to the plastic surgery department at the John Radcliffe in Oxford. Finally discovered what many had missed (but Dr Caroline had all the time suspected) – that I'd torn a tendon off my little finger. I was offered an operation – grafting a tendon from foot to hand. It may not work, Sara the surgeon told me. I was not at all keen on that, so was given an alternative: 450 finger exercises a day might cause other muscles and tendons to compensate for the one I'd lost. I'm certainly up for that!

August 2018
Monday 27   *Dubai and looking forwards*

Set off for Dubai this morning, my first long-haul overseas trip for well over a year. Two days of presenting talks to teachers.

And finally, the solution to these troubled thoughts has come to me. This persistent questioning can be flipped around and put to very good use. I'm going through my talks and re-examining everything. Do I mean what I think I mean? Is that point really clear? Am I illustrating that concept with the most appropriate examples? Am I making risky assumptions? Are my arguments and philosophies being delivered in as logical a fashion as they might be?

*And, of course, I can ask teachers these same kinds of questions. Is what they are doing really working? Are their explanations really clear and sufficiently differentiated for **all** their different pupils, with their different learning speeds? Are they using the best repertoire? Have they investigated what's new out there? Are **they** making risky assumptions? And so it goes on.*

And so indeed does my life go on ... I wasn't sure about that just weeks ago. But it is indeed a new beginning, with an unwritten future. How very, very exciting.

. . .

Journey's end?

Some reflections on an extraordinary experience

One thing I have been doing a lot of over these long months, is thinking. So, to bring my journal to a conclusion, here are some brief reflections on the main leitmotifs that have filled my mind and my life since January 2018 and how my relationship with each has gone through some profound changes.

If I had to list these leitmotifs, it would probably begin with *identity*, or maybe more accurately, one's *sense* of identity, and how vulnerable and fluid that identity actually is. What *really* defines who we are? Our appearance? What we do? Our skill set? How we use our skills and talents? What we think others think of us? The digital age young person may feel *their* identity is much bound up with their various status symbols – we are what we possess.

In fact, extreme illness has taught me that our identity is indeed multi-faceted but inextricably linked to our *reactions*. How I react is who I am. How I react to situations; to what people say; to what they do; to what they might write. That, I think, is the essence of identity – the other factors are secondary.

Who we are is how we react; and taking that one step further – not only is it how we react but also having some awareness of the effect of that reaction. Caring about how the recipient of our actions might feel. In my opinion, this perception of identity can have a profound impact both on the way we behave and, if we are teachers, on the effectiveness of our teaching.

I've also been aware that the *essence* of myself has metamorphosed from that of the normality I used to know, through being a dutiful patient to a new resurgent me that I feel is going to take some months to fully form. Having had such an overwhelming experience, having confronted my own mortality and having survived, I feel I don't want to return to quite the person I was. It's actually rather refreshing to feel comfortable with change.

I feel my confidence has taken a bit of a knocking over these difficult months – my confidence to do things. From simple things like answering an email to more complicated challenges like travelling around the world and presenting workshops. But happily, that confidence has returned.

Some weeks ago I would be watching other people going about their normal lives and thinking about how they all take their energy for granted. In fact, how we take so many things for granted. Things like each new day, contributing to life, eating and drinking and being able to enjoy the taste of what we eat and drink, sleeping, mobility, thought and especially friendship. Cancer causes you to think very differently about all these things. It focuses the mind and compels you to appreciate everything much more intensely. The new me will certainly appreciate *everything* to a much deeper level.

There's the immense part *friendship* and *sharing* have played, and my leitmotif list would also have to include dealing with *isolation* – something so alien to my natural state. Then there's *transformation* and ultimately, and happily, *survival*. Each of these notions are so much more meaningful to me now.

Then there's all the **learning** I've done – the past months have taught me much and have had a considerable effect on my understanding of the teaching process. They've taught me that it's okay not to be in control all the time. When virtually each week has brought serious new challenges you simply have to go with the flow. Flow and control – aren't they opposites? Or at least mutually exclusive. Well, no actually. And I've learnt how to balance these two life forces. I've also been thinking about applying this balance to teaching.

In lessons, many teachers like to be in control but we **must** *also go with the flow. Everyone we teach is different. Recognizing each individual's needs, acknowledging each response, and then responding back appropriately, are central to really successful teaching and learning. Teachers with a fixed agenda and style ('I know best, this is what's going to happen and it's going to happen like this …') are never really going to allow more than a handful of their pupils to succeed.*

I've learnt to be very patient. Cancer treatment moves slowly (and many cancer treatments are much more drawn out than mine). I'm not talking here about managing momentary impatience, but something much more longer term. I think it's got a lot to do with *expectation*. Learning to manage expectation, fully accepting that what will be, will be. Being as realistic as possible and then going with the flow (there's flow again – it's so important!). I haven't indulged in meditation – though I can see the benefits. But instead maybe I've fashioned my own kind of meditation.

Thinking through the reality of the situation and coming to terms with it seems to help solve the patience conundrum. This of course is essential in teaching. Pupils and parents are often impatient. And all parties concerned have expectations (teacher, pupil and parent) – and they are often unrealistic. Trying to bring some realistic and synchronised thinking to any teaching situation will really help reduce impatience and will really begin to instil happy and contented learning.

I've learnt about fear and trying to deal with it. Of course there's fear of death: the ultimate fear. But there's also fear of the unknown – people, situations, the future. Fear of not being able to do all the things that mean so much to me – sharing my love of music and wanting others to know how much it can enhance life in so many ways. During these past months I've learnt, as best as

I can, to let go of negative fears and not to be restricted by them. To accept the thoughts and simply enjoy what I can do now, and do it as profoundly as possible.

I've learnt about words – the words we use to express our thoughts; the words we use when we comment on another person's condition; the way we say thank you … the way we say virtually everything! Their effect, both spoken and written, can be so much more significant and far-reaching than we might ever think. Teachers and medics should always think very carefully about their words. And the way in which they are spoken.

I've learnt a lot about empathy. For really effective communication to take place we have to do our best to truly understand the person or persons with whom we are communicating. We have to try to understand and enter the myriad of parallel universes that are people's lives. Once I felt I had entered the world of all the wonderful doctors and nurses who have been looking after me (entered their worlds to the best of my ability, anyway!) I was able to communicate so much better. I felt comfortable discussing any and all issues. There was no block. Yet again there was flow. What an important ingredient that is!

And it's the same with pupils – we must try to understand them, their learning speed, their levels of motivation, what makes them tick musically. It's those considerations that will begin to empower the ability to communicate really effectively – the most important quality of the Virtuoso Teacher.

And what about the essence of what the Virtuoso Teacher does? I have also formed further insights here. I'm not a fan of comparisons, but by comparing the teacher with the doctor, some interesting thoughts have emerged. While doctors are fundamentally concerned with making their patients better, teachers are concerned with causing their pupils to make themselves better. Teaching them to learn how to learn. Helping them become independent and confident but without conceit, inflated ego or self-importance. And whilst, unreservedly, we trust and believe in both our doctor and our teacher, we need our teacher to cause us to believe in ourselves. That is what the true Virtuoso Teacher can do.

But there is something very important the teacher must learn from the doctor. In my experience, it seems to me that the doctor's desire to cure is unconditional: the teacher's desire to teach should also be unconditional. I wonder if this is always the case? And I'm thinking both of medics and teachers. I wonder if there are any who don't believe this to be so? Maybe there are … but in both medicine and teaching, I would hope such people are few and far between.

. . .

Illness, learning and teaching ... I began this journal by calling them three intimately connected and momentous energies. Illness is indeed draining, challenging and exhausting, but it needn't be a negative force. None of us would ever desire illness, of course, but if illness does invade our lives, much better to endeavour to treat it with acceptance and positivity.

Through much thought, some of which I have tried to describe in these pages, illness has caused me to reassess the enormous significance of learning and teaching. This significance is even greater than I had previously considered.

We can all learn and indeed should never let a day go by without doing so. We can all teach, and we don't need to be labelled 'teacher' to do so. A teacher is a guide and teaching is about communicating, inspiring and enthusing others to live life to the full. And we can all aspire to teach with compassion, benevolence and humanity. Learning and teaching represent a powerful undercurrent that can run through our entire lives – irrespective of the particular direction our lives happen to take us. When we learn and teach to the best of our ability we can truly contribute, to some degree, to the greater good of the world.

· · ·

Writing this journal has been wonderful therapy. It was my friend Richard Crozier's idea and though I was a little sceptical at first it has proven a hugely important part of my life. Getting these thoughts from brain to paper has given me a powerful sense of release. It has literally allowed me to move all these feelings out of my mind, to a place where I can be just a little more objective and detached about them. Sharing them, on paper and with friends, has been vital in maintaining sanity. I hope they may be helpful to others too – perhaps to those who may be facing a similar gruelling and life-changing ordeal.

Ultimately, this extraordinary and unexpected experience has profoundly reinforced my desire to live life as fully as possible; it's made me acknowledge that each day really is precious; it's made me want to contribute as much as possible; and, above all, it's taught me to take nothing for granted.

. . .